THE
ILLUSTRATED ENCYCLOPAEDIA
OF ANIMAL LIFE

THE ANIMAL KINGDOM

The strange and wonderful ways of
mammals, birds, reptiles, fishes and
insects. A new and authentic natural
history of the wild life of the world

VOLUME 13

FREDERICK DRIMMER, M.A.
EDITOR-IN-CHIEF

GEORGE G. GOODWIN
*Associate Curator of Mammals,
The American Museum of Natural
History*

CHARLES M. BOGERT
*Curator of Amphibians and Reptiles,
The American Museum of Natural
History*

**DEAN AMADON
E. THOMAS GILLIARD**
*Associate Curators of Birds,
The American Museum of Natural History*

CHRISTOPHER W. COATES *Curator*
JAMES W. ATZ, *Assistant Curator
Aquarium of The New York Zoological
Society*

JOHN C. PALLISTER
Research Associate, Insects, The American Museum of Natural History

ODHAMS BOOKS LONDON

Colour photographs supplied by members of The Free Lance Photographers Guild except as otherwise individually credited.

The Bluegill, *Lepomis macrochirus*, is rapidly becoming the most important of all the sunfishes. Not only has it been introduced into practically every state of the United States because of its fine-flavoured flesh and habit of readily taking both ordinary baits and dry flies, but it is also considered one of the best species to use in the fast growing activity of culturing fishes in ponds for food and various sporting activities.

Farmers and other landowners have gradually become aware of the fish pond as an unexploited source of cheap, delicious food and relaxing sport. But in order to harvest a full aquatic crop from any pond, it is necessary to plant, fertilize, and reap it properly—just as with any crop that grows on land. By stocking a pond with a correct proportion and amount of bluegills and largemouth black bass it is possible to obtain maximum annual yields of both species without having ever to replace them. The fertilizer that is spread through the water encourages the growth of enormous numbers of microscopic floating plants, which provide food for small crustaceans, snails, aquatic insects, and insect larvae. These creatures are in turn eaten by the bluegills. The last link in this food-chain is the largemouth that feeds on the bluegill.

The reason why it is important to put the proper proportion of the two kinds of fishes into a pond is that a balance must be struck between them. If there are too many largemouths, they will eat up all the bluegills and then cease to grow, becoming half starved and stunted. If there are too many bluegills, they, too, will become stunted for lack of food. Although too small for the pan, they will nevertheless grow large enough to reproduce, and will become so numerous that they eat up all the eggs of the largemouth. Eventually there will be nothing left in the pond but a population of dwarfed bluegills. In some parts of the United States, the bluegills always outrun the largemouths, unless introduced in such a small minority that they cannot become established at all, and in these regions the red ear sunfish, *Lepomis microlophus*, is preferred by most farmers and landowners. It has been established that a correctly handled one-acre pond can produce more than two hundred pounds of fish a year. This production level can be reached without any fertilization in some instances.

Adult bluegills average less than a pound, but one-and-one-half-pound individuals are not especially rare in nature. The largest specimen

EAL / 13—A

on record weighed four and one-half pounds and was fifteen and one-half inches long.

From May through October the bluegill spawns. The males often nest in colonies and each male guards his nest and eggs or young assiduously. As many as four thousand young may arise from a single nest. The bluegill hybridizes with at least seven other members of its families. So far as known, all the hybrids are sterile, except a very few fertile ones resulting from the cross with the red ear sunfish.

The Striped Bass, *Roccus saxatilis,* is now at home on both the Atlantic and Pacific coasts of the United States, thanks to man. Originally it lived close along the Atlantic shore from Florida to the Gulf of St. Lawrence. But in 1879 a shipment of less than 150 young specimens was made to California, and three years later about three hundred more were introduced. Now it is quite possible that there are more striped bass living on the west coast than in their native waters in the east! Several million pounds are caught by anglers each year. None is taken commercially off California because the commercial fishing of striped bass has been forbidden in that state since 1935. Along the Atlantic coast many of these fish are captured by both anglers and commercial fishermen.

Spawning in the striped bass takes place in the spring, when males two or more years old and females four or more years old enter fresh or nearly fresh waters, sometimes not very far from the sea, to reproduce. Groups of them gather at the surface, milling, splashing, and partly rolling on their sides, and during these activities the eggs are laid. Eggs are very numerous; about a million are produced by a ten-pound female. They just barely sink, and while they are lying on the bottom, the slightest current or eddy lifts them up and swirls them around. They hatch in about two to six days, depending on the temperature. After spawning has been completed, the adults return to the sea.

Some striped bass on the Atlantic coast migrate extensively, going north in the spring and south in the autumn, but the great majority of their spawnings occurs from New Jersey south. Their growth is rapid; at the age of two years a weight of half a pound is attained; at four years, more than two pounds. The largest striped bass ever taken by an angler weighed fifty-seven pounds and was fifty-five and one-half inches long, but the largest one of which there is any kind of authentic record is reported to have weighed 125 pounds. Males grow more slowly than females. The food of the striped bass consists of a large variety of smaller fishes and crustaceans.

The Black Sea Bass, *Centropristes striatus,* is one of more than four hundred members of the large family of true sea basses, the Serranidae. This group includes the groupers and hinds from salt water, the white and yellow basses from fresh water, and the striped bass and white perch that live in both kinds of water. The great majority of fishes in this family inhabit temperate or tropical seas, however. The black basses, it should be noted, belong to a separate group of fishes.

Black sea bass are popular with so-called "deep-sea fishermen", since they inhabit rocky bottoms at least a couple of fathoms deep and take the hook regularly. They are also of some importance as a commercial foodfish. They seldom exceed four pounds, although the record angler's catch weighed more than eight pounds.

The black sea bass straggles as far north as Maine and occurs as far south as Florida and rarely the Gulf Coast, being most common off the Middle Atlantic States. It feeds on squid, crabs, and other fishes.

Reproduction takes place in the late spring. The eggs are pelagic, that is, they float freely at the surface of the open ocean, and are slightly more than one thirty-second of an inch in diameter. They hatch in about five days. Males are more brightly coloured than females being blue-black with bright blue and white spots here and there. Older males develop a fatty hump over the back of the head during the breeding season. Its function is unknown. Males are larger than females and live to be at least twenty years old, whereas no females over half that age have been discovered. Among younger fish females predominate, but among the older ones males are much more numerous. A microscopic examination of the internal organs of numbers of black sea bass revealed that after the fifth year or so, many females gradually turn into males! So far as known, no sex-reversed individual functions both as male and female at one time. Instead, many black sea bass start out as egg-producers and later in life become functioning males.

The Spotted Jewfish, *Promicrops itaiara,* is the largest of all the American groupers—it may reach a weight of 750 pounds. Most are considerably smaller, however. In all, there are nearly forty different kinds of groupers and grouper-like fishes in the salt waters off the south-eastern and Gulf coasts of the United States, and the West Indies. Many of them are used for food; they are usually caught by hook-and-line. The spotted jewfish is no exception, being regularly eaten in Key West.

This species feeds on other fishes and on spiny lobsters. Those 350-pound specimens kept in the New York Aquarium seemed especially fond of dogfishes, which they swallowed whole. One of these giant jewfish would slowly approach an unwary two-and-one-half-foot dog-fish and suddenly open wide its jaws. The dogfish, sucked into the gaping maw by the strong current produced, would quickly and com-pletely disappear. At other times the large fish simply lay on the bottom and waited until a likely morsel swam by, before opening its cavernous mouth to engulf it. Presumably these are the ways spotted jewfish feed in nature, since they are sluggish and are usually found on the bottom of the sea near coral formations and sunken wrecks or under rocky ledges.

They occur on both the east and west coast of tropical America, from Florida to Brazil, and from Lower California to Peru.

Although the spotted jewfish possesses limited powers of altering its coloration, many other groupers are phenomenal quick-change artists. For example, the Nassau Grouper, *Epinephelus striatus*, has at least eight different colour phases, ranging from cream to dark brown. The fish can assume them at a moment's notice, and may show several in the course of a minute. The spotted jewfish can take on four colour patterns: dusky black, dark grey with black blotches, creamy white with black blotches, and almost entirely creamy white.

As many as six distinct patterns have been seen in individuals of some species of fishes within only a few moments. These remarkably rapid transformations result from the contraction and expansion of the pigment in thousands of tiny pigment cells in the skin of the fish. There are four or five different kinds of them distributed in various ways over the body. The multitude of colour changes are produced by the pigment expanding and contracting in different combinations. Some fishes definitely change their colours to match their surround-ings. In these the ability to alter their pigment patterns appears to help protect them from enemies, but in the groupers—and many other fishes, too—the colour patterns seldom seem to hide the fish. What purpose they serve, if any, is unknown. All that we can be certain of is that some patterns are definitely associated with flight, hiding, resting, fighting, and other activities.

Very little is known about the life history of the groupers save that they lay eggs, supposedly in the spring.

The Tilefish, *Lopholatilus chamaeleonticeps,* was the victim of one of the most famous of natural disasters known to have overtaken a fish. The species was not discovered until 1879, when a cod-fishing vessel happened to catch some in deep water of Massachusetts. Since it was a large fish of good commercial possibilities, it was investigated by the United States Bureau of Fisheries and found to be abundant within a circumscribed area ranging from about 90 to 150 fathoms in depth, all of a rather definite water temperature. Hardly had the new fishery become established, however, when vessels, arriving in New York from Europe, in 1882, reported seeing vast numbers of dead and dying fish, most of them tilefish. Perhaps 7,500 square miles of sea were covered by these fishes; at least one and half a billion dead tilefish were seen.

As far as known, the catastrophe was caused by a sudden, drastic but short-lived drop in water temperature brought about by some meteorological or geological event. For ten years not a tilefish was caught, and it was believed that the species had become extinct. But, in 1892, eight fish were taken. From then on their numbers gradually increased until, by 1916, over eleven and one-half million pounds were being taken annually. Since that time, however, the demand for tilefish has fallen off to such an extent that it is at present hardly ever commercially fished.

The coloration of the tilefish is most attractive. Its back is bluish green and its sides yellow or pink, both dotted with yellow. Its belly is rose and white, and its head is reddish towards the top, white below. It has a large well-toothed mouth and a peculiar, stiff, triangular, fatty flap projecting upward just in front of the long dorsal fin. Tilefish may reach a weight of fifty pounds, but the usual maximum weight is somewhat less.

Tilefish live on or near the bottom and feed on bottom-dwelling invertebrates, crabs being the most important single item of food. Occasionally they eat other fishes. Spawning takes place in the summer, and the small eggs float. The family Malacanthidae, to which the tilefish belongs, is principally found in tropical seas. Most of its members are smaller than the tilefish, not exceeding eighteen inches, and none possess the adipose, or fatty, flap.

The Bluefish, *Pomatomus saltatrix,* has been likened to an animated chopping machine. When a school of these ferocious, streamlined, sharp-toothed killers moves into a school of mackerel, menhaden, or herring, the carnage is truly colossal.

Instead of completely devouring their prey, the bluefish swing through the group, wildly biting and slashing, and leaving most of their victims with half a body or with great pieces bitten out of them. When their stomachs are filled, they apparently disgorge what they have eaten and begin all over again. Like blood-crazed dogs running amok in a herd of sheep, they seem to kill only for the joy of killing. After two unusually large schools of predator and prey have met, the trail of blood and maimed fish floating on the sea has been said to stretch for miles. When feeding inshore, bluefish have been known to drive thousands of menhaden right out of the water on to the beach.

Young bluefish, called snappers, emulate their parents, but do almost all of their feeding inshore, and on smaller prey. They grow rapidly, more than doubling their length in about three months during the summer. Just where or when they are spawned is not known. Ripe bluefish are occasionally taken during the late spring or summer on the Atlantic Coast, so it is presumed that reproduction takes place around that time. What little evidence there is, indicates that the eggs are laid over the continental shelf (the off-shore, underwater plain bordering a continent), perhaps fairly close to shore in some instances.

The demand for bluefish usually exceeds the supply—both at the fish market and among anglers. Roughly six million pounds are caught by commercial fishermen each year, and probably an equal amount by anglers. The fish are taken principally with nets or by trolling. Bluefish weighing fifty pounds were reported to have been taken in the old days, but today's maximum is only half that size.

We do not always find the bluefish where we would expect to. Although it is a widely distributed oceanic fish, there are large parts of the sea from which it is completely absent. Bluefish roam the temperate and tropical Atlantic, regularly travelling as far north as Maine during the summer and appearing off Florida and the Gulf Coast during the cold months. This north-and-south migration does not always closely follow the thermometer, however; the movements of bluefish are to a certain extent erratic, and independent of the temperature of the water in which they live. Bluefish are also found off the east coast of South America, on both sides of Africa, in the Mediterranean Sea, in the Indian Ocean, and around Australia. This fish is rare through most of the East Indies and completely absent in the Central and North Pacific. It is the only member of the family Pomatomidae, and is distinguished from all other fishes on the basis of internal features and a unique combination of external ones.

The Horse Mackerel, or Saurel, *Trachurus trachurus*, is not a mackerel, but belongs to the family of jacks. It is an oceanic fish, widely distributed in the Atlantic, rare to the west and north but common to the east and south. Its most distinguishing feature is a series of large scutes, or plates, that cover the lateral line from head to tail. This structure has a sharp dip in it about half-way down the fish's body.

The tiny buoyant eggs are laid during the summer. The young, which are less than one-eighth of an inch long when hatched, apparently live near the surface of the open sea at all times. From a size of about half an inch to nearly three inches, they are frequently found around jellyfish, under whose umbrella they take shelter. The horse mackerel feeds upon young herring and pilchard and at times large schools of them have appeared offshore to feed. It reaches a length of thirty inches and is caught commercially on the west coast of South Africa.

The jacks, scads, pompanos, runners, pilot fish, banded rudder fish and yellowtail, as well as the horse mackerel, are members of the family Carangidae. More than two hundred species are known from all the tropical and warm temperate seas of the world. Several species run many miles up tropical rivers. Practically all are edible, and some are taken in sufficient numbers to be important food fishes. They are strong swimmers and often take the hook avidly, being therefore popular with sportsmen.

The Pilot Fish, *Naucrates ductor*, frequently follows ships and large fish, especially sharks. The ancient Greeks believed that it would guide sailors who had lost their way at sea, showing them how to reach port. Whales, too, were supposed to be guided by pilot fish. This fish also played a part in classical Greek mythology and was held sacred in some places.

Observations in nature and in public aquariums have shown these beliefs—still held today by numbers of people—to be erroneous. The pilot fish does accompany slow-moving vessels and sharks, sometimes remaining very close to them for long periods of time. The reason for this behaviour cannot very well be to guide the ship or large fish, however, because the pilot fish *follows* rather than leads. The prospect of scraps from the ship's galley or odd bits from the shark's roughly torn prey is a much more likely reason for the peculiar attraction. Moreover, oceanic fishes of several sorts seem to be drawn to floating objects, and some species are characteristically found resting or idling under them.

Scientists suggest that living in the open ocean, where there are very few things to see, has made these fishes especially sensitive and likely to be attracted to any object that comes into view.

The young of the pilot fish frequently take shelter beneath floating seaweed and jellyfish or among the stinging tentacles of siphonophores like the infamous Portuguese man-of-war. These small pilot fish look so different from the adult that for a long time they were thought to be different species. Instead of being streamlined, they are short, rather grotesque creatures with relatively enormous eyes and numerous spines about the head. They are hatched from small, floating eggs.

The trim body of a grown pilot fish is distinctly marked with five broad, dark vertical bands. The four small spines placed just in front of the dorsal fin and the keel on each side of the base of the tail fin are also characteristic. A size of at least two feet is attained. The pilot fish ranges throughout the tropical and warm temperate seas of the world.

The Common Pompano, *Trachinotus carolinus*, is perhaps the most renowned of American tropical marine foodfish and one of the outstanding epicurean delights among seafoods. Its average weight is not more than two pounds, and less than a million pounds are marketed annually. The demand exceeds the supply, however, and many more pounds would be consumed if more fish could be caught.

The finely scaled body of the common pompano has its dorsal and anal fins almost identically located and both fins have their first few rays prolonged into a sharp-pointed, triangular extension so that one fin seems a mirror-image of the other. The colour of the common pompano is bluish green above, shading into silver below, with yellowish fins.

The fish are often prevalent near the surf. Young specimens are frequently thrown on the beach, where they flip-flop back towards the sea, to be picked up and carried away by the next wave. Young pompanos are hardy and can live out of water longer than many other species. Common pompanos feed on the eggs and young of other species and on various kinds of shellfish. When adult, they have very few teeth or none at all, but their small bony jaws apparently serve them quite adequately. Nothing is known of the pompano's reproductive habits, save that an extended spawning season during the late spring and early summer is indicated on the Gulf Coast.

POPULAR ON THE TABLE

The common pompano, which dwells along the Gulf and southern Atlantic coasts of North America, is highly esteemed as a foodfish. Pompanos are common near beaches, and young ones are often washed ashore. Flippity-flop, the fish make their way back to where the water will engulf them again. The adult pompano, pictured above, may grow to a length of eighteen inches.

The Yellowtail, *Seriola dorsalis*, schools off the coast of California and southward. It takes live or trolled bait eagerly and is noted for its long rapid runs when hooked. Commercial fishermen employ purse seines to catch yellowtail off the Mexican coast, but are prohibited from using this method in California waters. The fish is sold both fresh and canned. The usual maximum size is about twenty pounds, but fish weighing more than eighty pounds are on record.

Although superficially it looks like a relative of the tunas, the yellowtail is a true member of the family Carangidae. Its spindle-shaped body is beautifully coloured, bluish above and silvery below, with a conspicuous yellowish band running from eye to tail. As befits so streamlined a fish, the yellowtail pursues such fast-swimming prey as mackerel and flying fish as well as sardines, herring, and shrimps. Spawning is said to take place in the spring, but practically nothing is definitely known about the life history of this fish.

The Dorado or Dolphin, *Coryphaena hippurus*, feeds on flying fishes. These often take to the air to escape, and the dorado has been described as flushing them like quail. Their flight into another element may frequently be to no avail, for the dorado often swims as fast as a flying fish can fly, and snaps up the hapless creature when it drops back into the water. The fastest accurate estimate we have of the dorado's speed is a little more than thirty-seven miles per hour, as measured from a moving ship. While in pursuit of prey, the dorado often leaps from the water itself.

Like a brilliantly coloured knife, this fish cuts through the water, its narrow, long, triangular body being admirably designed to offer little water resistance. Its powerful tail is tipped with a deeply forked caudal fin, and along the whole back runs a soft, many-rayed dorsal. Larger specimens, especially males, have very high foreheads that may rise almost perpendicular to the long axis of the body. Because young specimens lack this character, they were originally described as different species. At one time, in fact, there were nearly a score of different kinds of dorado listed; now it is believed that there is only one species, or at the most two. They make up a family of their own, the Coryphaenidae.

Dorados are renowned for their coloration. A group of them can fill the water with electric blue flashes, it has been said. Luminous blues, royal purples, radiant greens and rich gold are all incorporated into their colour scheme. This changes so rapidly that it practically defies description, save to say that the fish's back is relatively dark and its belly quite light. Soon after capture, the vivid colours fade, going through a whole series of striking variations—as if some secret fire within the fish had been extinguished, leaving the exterior gradually to cool.

IN PURSUIT OF THE FLYING FISH

The dorado, a large, powerful fish of the warm seas, will frequently launch itself into the air as it pursues its favourite prey, the flying fish. A speedy swimmer, the dorado will also swim along below the fish in flight, and seize it when it descends to the water. The flesh of dorados is succulent, and they enjoy considerable popularity as gamefish.

Within recent years the dorado has become a popular gamefish. The largest one ever caught on hook-and-line weighed sixty-seven and one-half pounds and was sixty-eight and one-half inches long; which is close to the maximum size the fish ever attains. Dorados are excellent eating, but not enough are caught to make them a regular market fish.

The dorado is an oceanic fish that is found in most warm seas. On the Atlantic coast of the United States it ranges as far north as Cape Cod and on the Pacific it is found off southern California. Little is known of the fish's life history. Undoubtedly it lays floating eggs, probably in the spring in the region of the West Indies. Partly grown individuals are frequently found in numbers around or under floating objects like logs or bunches of Pacific kelp or Atlantic sargassum weed and gulf weed. The ancients took advantage of this habit and set bundles of reeds in the water to attract dorado, which were then caught with hook-and-line.

The Grey Snapper, *Lutjanus griseus,* has often been called the most intelligent of fish. Described as wary, alert, strong, swift, and adaptable, it has been held up as an excellent example of the highest development in modern, spiny-rayed fishes.

Grey snappers can be found throughout the West Indies and Bermuda, where they often are the most noticeable element in the fish population. North of Florida the species occurs only as a straggler, although it has been picked up as far north as New Jersey. To the south it is found along the coast of Central and South America to Brazil. Shaped like a typical spiny-rayed fish with a single dorsal fin, pelvic fins far forward and its large jaws armed with sharp teeth, the grey snapper seems well equipped to meet the necessities of underwater existence. Its usual maximum size is five pounds, but individuals weighing as much as eighteen pounds have been reported.

In behaviour the grey snapper reminds one of nothing so much as a man with an eye always to the main chance. Groups of them can be found around docks, stones, mangrove swamps, and coral reef formations, hungrily alert for any food that might become available. They usually do their hunting at night, however, feeding on crabs, shrimps, squid, worms, and small fishes. They sometimes can also be seen actively feeding during the day, however. A grey snapper will slowly stalk its prey until from one to three feet away from it. Then with a sudden burst of speed it dashes forward, seizes the unfortunate victim, turns sharply, and returns more slowly to the general area from which the rush was started, to await more food. Bits of floating seaweed are often examined intently for some morsel that might be lurking in them. Grey snappers will swim close to shore, paralleling the course of people walking along the beach, so they can catch the crabs that, frightened by the people, scuttle into the water. Scraps of all sorts from kitchen or galley are avidly taken—even such things as bread, potatoes, and beans, that one would suppose to be not very tasty to a fish which lives chiefly on animal food.

Because of their obvious alertness and aggressiveness, grey snappers have been employed in experiments by scientists interested in animal behaviour. It has been discovered that they can distinguish between various colours and patterns of their prey and can easily be taught to avoid certain types by associating them with a distasteful flavour, or other unpleasant stimulus provided by the experimenter.

In some places grey snappers can hardly ever be caught with hook-and-line, but in others they are not so wary. They are hard fighters when hooked and are used for food.

The Lutjanidae, the family of snappers, comprises some 250 species of fishes from tropical and warm temperate ocean waters, mostly near shore. They are hard-hitting, flesh-eating fishes, and provide good sport when hooked. A number are extensively used for food, including the Mutton Fish and the Schoolmaster of the West Indies.

The Red Snapper, *Lutjanus aya*, ranks with the pompano as one of the most famous foodfish of tropical marine waters. It is also renowned for its lovely rose-red colour; a red snapper served for dinner on a well-garnished plate looks as marvellous as it tastes. This bright colour distinguishes it from most other snappers, but there is at least one other species of red-coloured snapper with which it has been confused.

The red snapper inhabits deep water in the Gulf of Mexico, the Caribbean Sea and adjoining regions. It is fished by hook-and-line. The principal area for the fishery is located on the Campeche Banks off the coast of Yucatan; other smaller banks are scattered off the Gulf Coast of the United States and Mexico. We know practically nothing about the life history of the fish. What little evidence there is indicates that it spawns in the deep water in late spring or summer. It is known to attain a weight of seventy-nine pounds.

The Bluestriped or Yellow Grunt, *Haemulon sciurus*, is usually striped with chrome-yellow and lavender-blue, but these bright colours can be temporarily lost, the fish becoming entirely grey. During the day bluestriped grunts gather in groups around coral formations and underwater growths, and at night they scatter to feed on small crustaceans, molluscs, worms, and brittlestars. Their range is from Florida and the West Indies southward to Brazil. They are also found in Bermuda.

As in many other grunts, the lining of the mouth is a brilliant red. Often, two bluestriped grunts will approach each other head on, and one will suddenly open wide its mouth, plainly displaying the bright interior. The other will then follow suit. Often the two will approach each other so closely that the top and bottom of their jaws touch. Then they will back off slightly and repeat the strange performance. The exact significance of their manoeuvres is not known, but it seems quite possible that they are a warning or recognition display by which the fish are told of the presence or intent of their fellows. Other species of grunts perform in a similar manner. The bluestriped grunt grows to a length of about one and one-half feet.

The grunts, family Pomadasyidae, are closely related to the snappers, differing from them most prominently in the arrangement of teeth. Like the snappers they inhabit tropical and warm temperate seas, are flesh-eaters and are much used for food. Among the grunts are the margates, porkfish, pigfish, and tomtate.

The Pigfish, *Orthopristis chrysopterus*, makes distinct grunting sounds when it is hooked, revealing by its behaviour as well as its appearance that it belongs to the grunt family. It is caught by both anglers and commercial fishermen, but is a foodfish of only minor importance. Usually it is most tasty, but once in a while an individual with a distinctly bad odour and taste turns up. This unpleasant quality is acquired by eating acorn-worms, which are peculiar worm-shaped creatures (not really worms at all), whose bodies are strongly scented with an evil-smelling chemical similar or identical to iodoform. The great majority of pigfish eat less odoriferous bottom-inhabiting creatures such as small crustaceans, bivalves, worms, and a few starfish.

At about two years of age pigfish spawn for the first time. They are then somewhat over eight inches long. At the latitude of North Carolina, spawning may begin as early as mid-March and extend through June, the height of activity occurring in May.

The female lays her eggs inshore early in the evening. They are perhaps half the size of a pinhead, float at the surface and hatch in about one and one-half to three days. The newly hatched pigfish is only about one-sixteenth of an inch long and floats helplessly on its back, with its relatively large yolk-sac uppermost. By the time it is three days old, it has absorbed practically all of the yolk, has assumed an upright position, has started to grow fins and is able to swim. It is of course still completely at the mercy of its surroundings and remains so for some time.

The pigfish occurs along the coast of the United States from Massachusetts to Texas, but it is uncommon north of Virginia. During the cold months it disappears from its usual inshore haunts, returning in the spring in a rather thin and run-down condition. Just where it spends the winter remains a mystery. The maximum size is about fifteen inches.

The Northern Scup, *Stenotomus chrysops*, often falls victim to otter-trawls, pound-nets, floating traps, purse-seines and hook-and-line, since there is a good demand for it. The otter-trawl—in which the net is spread apart by two large boards—accounts for most of the catch. Some twenty million pounds of northern scup are sold commercially each year.

These fish spawn in the bays and other inshore waters of southern New England and the Middle Atlantic States from May to August. The tiny buoyant eggs hatch in forty hours at 72 degrees F. The larvae are less than one-eighth of an inch long; by their first winter they have grown to about three inches. Adult northern scup average about one pound. Scup are bottom feeders, and gather in groups to eat crustaceans, molluscs, worms, and small fishes.

The Sparidae or porgy family, to which the northern scup and the sheepshead belong, contains more than one hundred different species. They are found mostly along tropical and warm temperate shores, but some live in quite cold water, especially around South Africa and southern Australia. Here the largest species seem to occur; for example, the Musselcracker, *Cymatoceps nasutus*, of South Africa grows to a weight of more than one hundred pounds. In these regions the sparids are among the most important fishes used for food.

Fishes of this family are also of commercial value along the east coast of North America and in the West Indies, the Mediterranean Sea and the Red Sea, in which regions the greatest number of species occurs. They are relatively rare in the western Pacific, still rarer in the central portion and on the west coast of South America, and are absent from the west coast of North America. A few of the sparids enter brackish and fresh water.

The Sheepshead, *Archosargus probatocephalus*, was once common around New York and was a commercially important species in Chesapeake Bay and on the coast of the Gulf of Mexico. To the regret of fishermen, it is now unknown in the vicinity of New York, has practically disappeared from Chesapeake Bay, and has greatly declined along the Gulf Coast. The reason for this striking decrease in abundance is a mystery.

The sheepshead has been recorded as far north as the Bay of Fundy, but it seldom appeared north of Cape Cod and then only during the summer and early autumn. From North Carolina southward it is a year-round resident. It occurs as far south as Tampico, Mexico. Very game when hooked, and very tasty when served, the sheepshead is popular with anglers and commercial fishermen. It reaches a length of thirty inches and a weight of twenty pounds, but averages no more than six.

The seven dark vertical bands on the body of the sheepshead are distinctive. The single dorsal fin is strongly spined, as is the anal. Prominent incisor teeth give its mouth a somewhat "buck-tooth" appearance. It has a long digestive tract of the kind usually associated with fishes that feed on vegetation, but it eats both aquatic plants and shellfish.

The eggs are very small and float, hatching in about forty hours at 77 degrees F. Spawning takes place in the spring. When they are only half an inch long, baby sheepsheads already resemble their parents. Their rate of growth is slow.

The Tripletail, *Lobotes surinamensis*, disappointing to relate, does not have three tails. Still, looking at it, you might almost think it lived up to its name—the rear portions of its dorsal and anal fins are quite large, and form, with the caudal fin, three distinct lobes, all about the same size, giving the illusion of three tail fins.

Adult tripletails are mottled dark brown; younger fish are lighter in colour. They reach a length of three and one-half feet and a weight of at least forty-one pounds. They are good eating, but are nowhere caught in sufficient quantity to make them a regular market fish. Tripletails frequent a variety of coastal regions, including the mouths of rivers—where they congregate around jetties, wrecks, fallen tree-tops, and so forth—and over rocky or coral bottoms. They range from Cape Cod to Florida and the Gulf Coast, and farther south. A few have been taken in the Mediterranean. They occur along the tropical east coast of Africa and the eastern Asiatic coast from southern Japan to Australia, including the East Indies. They are also occasionally found in other warm ocean waters.

The spawning of the tripletail is believed to occur during the late

SPAWNING OF THE FIGHTING FISH

Under the bubble nest he has built, a male Siamese fighting fish clasps his darker-coloured mate
as her eggs sink slowly through the water. (Please turn page.) See *page 1562.*

A QUICK RETRIEVE

The male turns and dashes down to pick the eggs up in his mouth—even before some of them reach the bottom. He then swims up and places them among the bubbles of his surface nest. The male fish continues to guard the young after they hatch, which event takes place in about two days, and to replace any babies that fall out of the nest. Siamese fighting fish are noted for their pugnacity. See page 1562.

New York Zoological Society Photos

Largest of the small sunfish, the average adult bluegill weighs less than a pound although one and one-half pound individuals are not especially rare. A fine-flavoured fish not too difficult to catch, it is also considered one of the best species for use in pond culture and is rapidly becoming the most important of all sunfishes. A one-acre pond, properly planted, fertilized and reaped can produce more than two hundred pounds of bluegills and largemouth black bass annually without restocking.

See page 1535

[13-1]

[13-1A]

The pearl gourami belongs to the air-breathing fishes known as the labyrinths because of the labyrinth-like series of plates in the paired air-chambers above their gills. This extra breathing device makes it possible for the gouramis and the related climbing perch, fighting fish and other bettas to live in sluggish waters of the swamps, small ponds, ditches and rice paddies of tropical Africa, south-eastern Asia, the East Indies and the Philippines. Many of the species average less than a foot in length and are popular as home aquarium fishes. (The smaller, long-spined fish is a freshwater "angel" from South America.) The giant gourami, which attains a length of two feet and a weight of twenty pounds, is cultivated as an important freshwater foodfish throughout south-eastern Asia from India to China.

See page 1559

The tiny, bristle-like cusp-bearing teeth of the angel fish give the order to which it belongs its scientific name, "Chaetodontoidei", which means literally "spiny-toothed". The salt-water angel and butterfly fish families include the vast majority of the more than 200 species of this order, the angel fishes in general being the larger, sometimes reaching a length of two feet. They are usually found in the coastal waters and around coral reefs in the East and West Indies.   See page 1565

[13-2]

The Moorish idol with its scimitar-shaped dorsal fin and bold black, yellow and white stripes is the exotic member of the scat family, near-kin to the angel and butterfly fishes. Scats regularly live in salt, brackish and fresh water, from the Red Sea through the Indian Ocean and the Western Pacific from Japan to Australia. The idols are generally found in the more tropical parts of this range. The yellow tang belongs to an entirely different group—the surgeon or doctor fishes which get their name from the lancet-shaped sharp spines near the base of the tail. Almost 100 species of this tropical-sea, coral-reef-dwelling fish are known, their chisel-shaped teeth, among other things, distinguishing them from their close neighbours.   See page 1566

[13-2A]

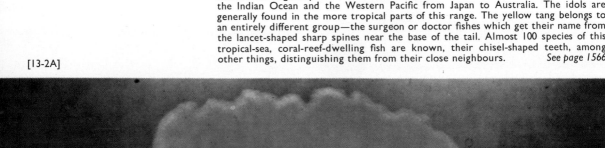

summer in the tropical western Atlantic. The eggs and larval fish have yet to be described. Young individuals about three and one-half inches long remarkably resemble dead leaves floating on the sea, not only in appearance but in behaviour. Observations of a small captive specimen revealed that it habitually lay on one side at the surface of the water, usually with its head slightly down, moving only by means of its transparent pectoral fins. If slightly disturbed, the fish seemed to rely on its deceptive resemblance, because it would move away quite slowly, never abandoning its posturing. If thoroughly disturbed, say by a net, it would dart away for about eighteen inches, then immediately resume its leaf-mimicking behaviour. When mangrove leaves were thrown into its tank, the small tripletail carefully moved over among them, in effect schooling with the leaves!

The tripletail belongs to the family Lobotidae, a small group of three or four species. Two of them are confined to salt, brackish, and fresh waters of India, Burma, south-eastern Asia and the East Indies, and one has been reported from the Pacific coast of Panama.

The Atlantic Croaker, *Micropogon undulatus,* is named for the noise that it produces. When the fish is out of water, the sound is like a very low, rasping croak, but under water it has been described as consisting of rapid drum rolls that resemble the distant sound of a pneumatic drill being driven into asphalt. It can be heard through at least twenty-five feet of water. The fish accomplishes this by rapidly vibrating the walls of its swim bladder (air bladder) by means of two special muscles attached to it. The swim bladder is apparently modified to provide a noise-making apparatus, having a peculiar shape with two hornlike extensions at the front end and a single taillike one at the rear.

Most members of the family Sciaenidae, to which the Atlantic croaker, the weakfishes, and the drums belong, are capable of producing sounds. The significance of this ability is not understood, although it may well have social import—that is, the fish may employ it to communicate with one another. Both male and female Atlantic croakers can produce sound, but the male's apparatus is more robust than the female's, and he is said to produce a louder sound. In the weakfish, only the male has the muscles necessary for noise production, or "drumming", as it is called.

The study of underwater fish sounds has become increasingly

important. With the development of hydrophones for listening beneath the surface in order to detect submarines and other vessels, it became necessary to recognize those sounds made by the natural inhabitants of an area, so that they might be accurately distinguished from those made by motors and propellers. The bottom of the sea turned out to be quite a noisy place, with snapping shrimps and a number of fishes being among the loudest of all aquatic life. We now have recordings of many of these sounds.

The underslung mouth, minute barbels on either side of the lower jaw, and slight extension of the middle of the tail fin distinguish the Atlantic croaker from other members of its family. The eggs of this fish have not yet been described, but studies on the condition of ripeness in grown fish and the appearance of very small ones in different localities indicate that spawning extends from August until January on the east coast of the United States, and from October to February on the Gulf Coast. This is an unusually long reproductive season for an egg-laying fish.

Croakers are one of the principal foodfish of the Middle Atlantic States. They are also extensively caught by anglers. They average about one pound, the maximum being five or more. Croakers themselves feed mostly upon small animal life, including crustaceans, worms, bivalves, and snails.

The family Sciaenidae includes several fishes of economic importance as foodfishes. There are about 150 species in all, most of them from shallow, warm, salt water. Some species venture into colder regions, however, some into mid-ocean and some into brackish water. A few tropical species live more or less permanently in fresh water. One species, the Freshwater Drum, *Aplodinotus grunniens*, occurs in streams and lakes from Guatemala to Canada.

The Red Drum or Channel Bass, *Sciaenops ocellata,* can be most readily recognized by the round black spot on the upper part of the base of the tail fin. This well-known food and game fish is found from New York to Texas, but exists in large numbers only south of Chesapeake Bay. The largest specimen ever caught with rod-and-reel weighed eighty-three pounds and was fifty-two inches long.

From the presence of ripe adults and the appearance of very young specimens, scientists judge that spawning takes place in the late autumn and winter. In Texas the height of the reproductive season apparently falls in October. The eggs and larvae are unknown, however. The principal food of the red drum is shrimps, crabs, and small fishes.

The Black Drum, *Pogonias cromis,* has been known to make so much noise, when gathered in a school near a ship at anchor, that it has kept sailors awake at night. The fish's swim bladder is especially well developed, with tough, thick walls, and attached to it are special muscles which, when contracted, cause the hollow sac to vibrate, producing the sound.

DRUMMER OF THE DEEP
The common drumfish, or black drum, which dwells along the Atlantic coast of the United States, is able to produce a drumming sound by contracting the muscles of its swim bladder. Note the barbels at the bottom of the fish's lower jaw; apparently these "feelers" help it locate the worms and shellfish on which it feeds.

Some black drums are caught commercially, mostly along the coast of Texas. Their average weight is, roughly, four pounds, but specimens weighing almost 150 are known. The fish is a bottom feeder, eating various bivalves such as clams, mussels, and oysters, and also crabs, shrimps, and worms. Large black drums crush the shells of these creatures with their strong, broad, pharyngeal (throat) teeth. Undoubtedly the numerous short barbels located on the under-side of the lower jaw aid in locating this bottom-dwelling food.

Spawning takes place mainly from February to May along the Gulf

Coast. Large specimens are very prolific; a forty-four-inch female contained more than five million eggs. Young black drums are marked with five wide, dark, vertical bars. These are lost during growth. Older fish are usually a uniform dusky grey although some are coppery in colour.

The Grey Squeteague or Weakfish, *Cynoscion regalis,* is a popular fish with both commercial and sports fishermen. About twenty-five million pounds are taken each year by the former alone. The range of the fish extends from Massachusetts to Florida along the Atlantic coast.

The weakfish gets its name from the character of its mouth and flesh—these are quite easily torn. Its jaws appear anything but weak, however, the lower one being quite prognathous (protruding) and the upper one having two large canine teeth, or fangs. The record weakfish ever caught by rod-and-reel weighed seventeen and one-half pounds and was nearly four feet long, but the average is considerably less than this.

Like other members of its family, the weakfish produces sounds, but only the males possess the necessary apparatus to do this. They are especially noisy around spawning areas during the reproductive season. Spawning takes place from May until September. The eggs are laid some distance offshore in certain places and inshore in others. They are buoyant and hatch in one and one-half days or a little longer. Maturity is usually attained at the age of two years. Food consists of various fishes, squid, and shrimps.

Quite extensive migrations up and down the coast are made by the grey squeteague, and during cold weather they seek deeper water. The fish generally travel in large groups, although they do not seem to be a schooling fish in the strict sense of the word, as are herring and mackerel.

The Spotted Squeteague, *Cynoscion nebulosis,* can be distinguished from the grey squeteague by the presence of conspicuous, round, black spots on the body and dorsal and caudal fins, and by the absence of small scales on the anal and second dorsal fins. It ranges from New York to Texas, but is rare north of Virginia. Like its more northern relative, it is an important food and game fish. It does not grow quite as large, however.

The White Sea Bass, *Cynoscion nobilis,* is not a bass at all, but is closely related to the weakfishes of the Atlantic. It is one of the most popular of all the marine game species on the Pacific coast of the United States and is also fished commercially. It reaches a length of at least five feet and a weight of eighty pounds. The record rod-and-reel catch nearly equalled this, weighing seventy-seven pounds, four ounces.

White sea bass range from south-eastern Alaska to southern California. They are uncommon north of San Francisco, however. Spawning takes place from March to August. Squid, crustaceans, and various fishes make up their food.

The Red Mullet, *Mullus surmuletus*, belongs to the group of goatfishes or surmullets, family Mullidae—it is not a true mullet. You can easily recognize these fishes by their bright golden, orange, or rose colours and by the two prominent fleshy barbels that hang down from the lower jaw. The great majority of the forty or so species range between eight and sixteen inches in length. Some are esteemed foodfishes. They inhabit the shores of all tropical seas, sometimes entering brackish or fresh water. A few species, such as the red mullet, are found in cool temperate waters.

We find red mullet from the Mediterranean Sea to Norway. They occupy the more northerly parts of their range during the warmer months. Their eggs are laid during the spring and summer to float in the open sea, and are slightly more than one thirty-second of an inch in diameter; they hatch in about one week. Like other goatfishes, the red mullet seeks its food on the bottom, apparently using its barbels to detect the molluscs, crustaceans, and worms upon which it feeds. It reaches a length of about fifteen inches.

This fish has been used for food since ancient times. The Romans sometimes paid fabulous prices for large specimens; one fish was equal to a slave in value, or even roughly equivalent to its own weight in silver. Red mullets were paraded around Roman banquet halls so that the guests might watch the beautiful play of colours over their bodies as they died. They were also kept in fishponds as pets, and it is reported that one wealthy fancier showed much more concern over the health of his fish than that of his slaves.

The Leaf-fish, *Monocirrhus polyacanthus*, drifts idly through the water, looking for all the world like a dead leaf. Its compressed body is roughly leaf-shaped, and is coloured tan or brown with appropriate mottlings, making it an excellent mimic of a leaf that has died and fallen from some bush or tree into the water. To complete the illusion, the fish has a single stout barbel on its chin that appears exactly like the dead leaf's stem. The pectoral fins and the rear portion of the dorsal and anal fins are so transparent that they are practically invisible. By vibrating these, the fish can glide through the water, seemingly propelled by imperceptible forces.

Sometimes the leaf-fish lies motionless on its side, but more often it rests quietly upright with its head lower than its tail. When some likely fish strays into its vicinity, the leaf-fish stalks it until close enough. Then, with a sudden dart, accompanied by the opening and closing of its great mouth, the larger fish completely engulfs the smaller one.

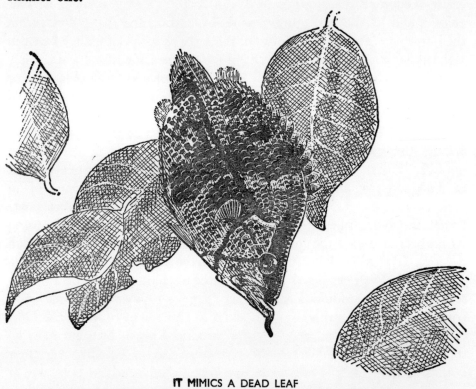

IT MIMICS A DEAD LEAF

It is hard to tell the leaf-fish from a dead leaf; its brownish, leaf-sized body glides through the water much as a leaf drifts, seemingly without effort. The smaller fish it stalks usually does not realize the enemy is at hand until escape is no longer possible.

The eggs of leaf-fish are attached to plants or stones by small individual stalks. They are fanned and guarded by one of the parents until they hatch, that is, for about three days. Leaf-fish inhabit the fresh waters of northern South America. They reach a length of about three and one-half inches.

Leaf-fish are members of the family Nandidae, a small group of freshwater fishes with a most peculiar geographical distribution. In India, south-eastern Asia and the East Indies there are five or six species, in west Africa there is one, and in northern South America and Trinidad there are two or three species, of which one or two are leaf-fishes. Scientists have been puzzled as to how this group of primarily freshwater inhabitants came to occupy three such widely isolated localities. The larger species, which are from Asia and reach a length of about eight inches, are used for food. Among these Asiatic forms, two or three are occasionally found in brackish water.

The Archer Fish, *Toxotes jaculatrix*, shoots its prey with drops of water. (It must have been named long ago, because the drops it shoots are more like bullets than arrows.) This fish cruises about the surface until it spots some likely insect resting on a leaf or bank near the water, then carefully manoeuvres into position, pokes its mouth up out of the water and squirts a series of well-aimed drops of water at the intended prey, usually knocking it into the water with the first few aquatic "bullets". Up to distances of four feet archer fish are almost one hundred per cent accurate. Large specimens—they reach lengths of eight to ten inches—can propel water as far as twelve feet.

On the outside, the archer fish gives us no clue as to how it performs these remarkable feats of marksmanship. Although its body shape is characteristic, it has no prolonged snout or other obvious apparatus for spitting water. Its mouth is not large and is angled downwards quite sharply, but is not very different from that of many other fishes that never expel drops of water. Its eyes are large but unspecialized.

Only when we examine the inside of the mouth do we discover the water-propelling mechanism. Running along the roof of the mouth is a narrow groove. The tongue is quite mobile and can be raised to fit against this, thus making a thin straight tube. Through this the fish forces water by quickly clapping down its gill-covers. The tip of the tongue probably acts as a valve.

The accuracy of this waterborne artillerist is truly marvellous, considering the complicating factors of refraction and distortion. The fish keeps its eyes under water while shooting and therefore must compensate for the change in direction of light rays as they pass from air into water, as well as the deformations resulting from ripples and other disturbances of the water's surface.

Archer fish eat water creatures as well as land creatures. They live in fresh and brackish waters, usually near the coast, of south-eastern Asia from India to the Philippines. Nothing is known of their reproductive habits except that they undoubtedly lay eggs and that newly hatched young are seen in May around Bangkok, Thailand. There are eight different species of archer fishes, all hailing from south-eastern Asia, Australia, and the islands of the south-west Pacific. They comprise the family Toxotidae.

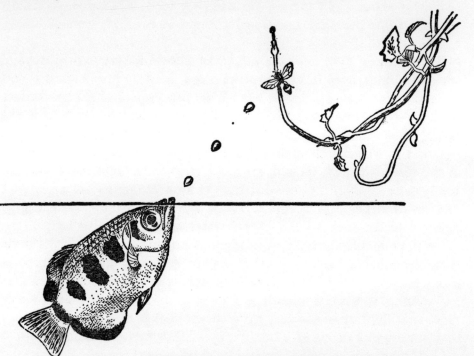

AN ARCHER OF UNUSUAL SKILL

The archer fish is one of the most extraordinary members of the animal kingdom—it actually brings down its prey with a missile. The victim, an insect on a leaf or a nearby bank, is toppled from its resting place by carefully aimed drops of water squirted from the fish's mouth. Seldom does the archer fish miss its mark.

Climbing Perch, Fighting Fishes, and Their Relatives

IF YOU never knew it before, by now you have observed that the fish world is far from humdrum. Its unexpected marvels startle the imagination. Once you take a close look at the fishes, you simply have to revise most of your fixed opinions about them. Even that standard symbol of helplessness, "a fish out of water", will not hold up against some of the strange realities to be told about in this chapter —fishes that are actually wayfarers on the land.

Most fishes, we have seen, are dependent on the gases dissolved in the water in which they live. They breathe by absorbing these gases into the bloodstream as the water passes around their gills. But the fishes in this group often do perfectly well with the air outside the water. They possess an extra breathing device—a pair of chambers above their gills. Some of these fishes have in the chambers a labyrinth-like series of plates, and it is from these that the order was named Labyrinthici.

Because they can breathe the air directly, these fishes manage to exist in places too warm or foul for the great majority of other fishes. We often find them in swamps, small ponds, ditches, and rice paddies —in the fresh waters of tropical Africa, south-eastern Asia, the East Indies, and the Philippines. Most average less than a foot in length. The larger species of the labyrinths—that is what we call the members of this order—are used for food.

The climbing perch, paradise fishes, various gouramis, and the Siamese fighting fish and other bettas belong to the family Anabantidae (this name comes from a word meaning "to go up", and most of these fishes do just that when getting a gulp of air). Some of its fifty or more species are popular tenants of the home aquarium. They are wonderful in many ways, not the least being the ritual that surrounds the laying of their eggs and the rearing of their young. Males of the

1559

Siamese fighting fish, the paradise fishes, and most of the gouramis make a floating nest of bubbles to hold the eggs. The giant gourami goes farther—it builds a nest of plants. By comparison, the climbing perch appears indifferent, for it lays floating eggs and does not care for them in any way. But the Cape kurper of South Africa guards its adhesive eggs, which are laid on stones or other submerged objects. In two or three species of bettas we find an odd quirk indeed: the males carry the eggs in their mouths until hatching.

Floating eggs are the rule with the snakeheads. The males of this group (family Ophicephalidae, with about thirty different species) forsake their otherwise savage habits at breeding time to stand guard over the eggs. The snakeheads are the largest of all the labyrinths; they rather resemble the North American bowfin in appearance, and one or two species grow as long as four feet. Much smaller is the pikelike *Luciocephalus pulcher* (a single species comprises the family Luciocephalidae). It is only about seven inches long, and dwells in south-eastern Asia and the East Indies. We believe it to be a mouth-breeder—that is, to carry its eggs and young in its mouth.

The Climbing Perch, *Anabas testudineus,* is often brought alive to market in a basket and can be kept alive out of water for a whole day, simply by sprinkling it with a little water from time to time. The fish breathes air by means of a pair of special cavities, located over the gill chambers and containing a series of thin, bony plates, arranged more or less in circles with a common centre. These plates are covered with a membrane that is provided with a good supply of blood; through them the fish gets its oxygen. Ordinary gills are also present, but are so reduced in size that the fish drowns if kept under water. It must regularly come to the surface to take a gulp of air.

Not only can the climbing perch live out of water, but it some-times voluntarily leaves its aquatic home to travel overland. It does this by extending its gill-covers out to the side and then flopping altern-ately to the left and right. The gill covers, with their backward projecting spines, prop the fish in a partly erect position and are alternately stuck into the ground, acting somewhat like a pair of short crutches as the fish hitches along. In spite of its jerky, ungraceful mode of getting about on land, the climbing perch can travel considerable distances—it has been known to cover three hundred feet in about thirty minutes.

Although its name would indicate otherwise, the climbing perch very rarely ascends the trunks of trees. Its overland trips are apparently made to find new or better bodies of water in which to live.

PORTRAIT OF A FISH OUT OF WATER

The climbing perch, a native of Asia and Africa, is a renowned land traveller. It possesses special breathing equipment which permits it to leave the water and journey overland in quest of a new place to live. To move about, the fish has unusual gill covers, which it uses much like crutches.

The climbing perch inhabits all sorts of fresh waters in south-eastern Asia from southern China to India, and in Ceylon, the Philippines and the islands of the East Indies. Feeding principally on insects, shrimps, and snails, it grows to be a little more than nine inches long. It is an important foodfish in many parts of the Orient. Climbing perch lay floating eggs, and the parents take no care of them. Other species of climbing perches are found throughout much of Africa.

The Giant Gourami, *Osphronemus goramy,* has been widely transplanted through much of the tropical Far East. So widely, in fact, that no one is sure just where the species originated—perhaps China was its natural home, or perhaps it was first found in south-eastern Asia and the East Indies. At any rate it is at present one of the most important freshwater foodfish in southern Asia from India to China, where it is extensively cultured in ponds.

Pondfish culture is an excellent way of obtaining cheap and palatable food of high protein content. This fact has only gradually been recognized and put into practice in Africa and North and South America. On the other hand, pondfish culture has been of great economic importance for some time in the Orient and in parts of the Middle East and Europe. In Indonesia alone there are at least three hundred thousand acres of fishponds, and in Poland there were perhaps two hundred thousand acres before the second World War.

The giant gourami attains a length of at least two feet and a weight of twenty pounds. It is primarily a vegetarian, but eats a good deal of animal matter if available. Being an airbreather, it can inhabit waters that are quite warm and stagnant.

Spawning may occur the year round. Male and female select some spot along the edge of their pool or some rocky crevice to use as a point of anchorage, and construct about it a nest made of aquatic plants. With their mouths they gather plants, carry them to the nesting area, and form them into a rather elaborate structure not unlike a bird's nest. Its shape varies, but it always has an opening on one of its lower sides. Its maximum dimensions are approximately twelve by fifteen inches, and it rests about six inches beneath the surface. Nest making occupies from a week to a month. Finally the female spawns, lying on her side while doing so. As many as two thousand lemon-yellow, buoyant eggs, a little less than one-eighth of an inch in diameter, are laid in the nest and then covered over with nesting material.

Both parents guard the nest, taking turns in watching it and circulating water around it by fanning with their fins. Hatching occurs in ten to fifteen days. The young are about three-sixteenths of an inch long when they first emerge from the eggs and float upside down at the surface. After two days they sink to the bottom, but remain belly upward. By the fourth or fifth day they are able to swim upright.

The Siamese Fighting Fish, *Betta splendens,* has been selectively bred for fighting and endurance by the Siamese for the past century. Other strains of this fish have been selectively bred by the Siamese and breeders in other nations for large fins and beautiful colours. The results of these two lines of endeavour are distinct types of fish, so different that at first glance they appear to belong to entirely separate species, although they can still interbreed.

Fighting fish that have been bred for fighting qualities are practically identical in appearance with the wild fish from which they were originally derived. Adult males, which are the fighters, reach a maximum length of about two and one-half inches. They are short-finned creatures, dull brown in colour except when displaying before a female or threatening another male. Then they show the most gorgeous array of reds, golds, blues and blacks, all delicately intermixed in a subtle yet definite pattern.

Wild fighting fish are pugnacious, and if two males are placed together in a tank, they will fight for perhaps as long as fifteen minutes. Specially bred fighting males, however, often fight continuously, with only brief respites in order to breathe, for as long as three hours, and they have been known to keep up a combat for as long as six hours before one of the adversaries finally refused to carry on the battle any farther. The fish attack one another with their small sharp teeth, tearing each other's fins and scales. The Siamese "fight" these fish like game-cocks; such contests have been popular sporting events in Thailand for several hundred years.

In contrast to the fighting strains, those fish bred for beautiful colours and shapely fins have lost some of their ability to do battle. Instead, the large males exhibit great, flowing dorsal, caudal, and anal fins that are sometimes longer than their bodies. Their colours include red, maroon, blue, green, and cream. Even in these showy strains, however, the females are quite uninteresting in colour and fins.

Wild Siamese fighting fish are found in ponds, ditches and other sluggish waters throughout Thailand. They feed on animal life, principally small freshwater crustaceans and insect larvae. They are said to be invaluable destroyers of larval mosquitoes. In Bangkok there are people who rear mosquitoes in order to sell the larvae to the numerous breeders of fighting fish there. Like other members of its group, the Siamese fighting fish is an air-breather and is thus capable of living in quite foul water or in very close quarters in captivity.

The male Siamese fighting fish builds a floating nest of froth by blowing innumerable small, sticky bubbles that cling together at the surface of the water. Male and female embrace under the nest, at which time a few eggs are laid. These are heavier than water, and as they sink the male swoops down, picks them up in his mouth, carries them up to the nest and places them among the bubbles. This procedure is repeated many times until two to seven hundred eggs are laid.

The male now stands guard beneath his froth raft, repairing it, driving other fish, including the female, away from it, and replacing any eggs that may fall out of it. When the young are hatched—in about 30 hours at 80° Fahrenheit—he replaces any of these, too, that tumble out of the nest. In a few days the young can swim well enough to leave their floating cradle, putting the parent's duties at an end. In captivity males are capable of breeding every three days for short periods of time; in nature they undoubtedly breed several times during a year. Occasionally in captivity, a female turns up who drives the male away from the nest after spawning and then takes charge of the eggs in truly masculine fashion—for fishes, that is.

The life span of the Siamese fighting fish in nature is about two years.

The Snakehead, *Ophicephalus striatus*, is sometimes fished with a knife. During the dry season, when the water of their pond or swamp evaporates, snakeheads go down into the mud and await the return of the rains. Siamese fishermen wade into the stiff mud and with their knives cut it away in layers in search of these fish.

Found in many places, from China and the Philippines to India and Ceylon, including the East Indies, snakeheads are among the most esteemed foodfish in the Orient. Because of their hardiness and ability to live out of the water, they are frequently brought to market in baskets. In countries where refrigeration is a rarity, such fish are a blessing. They offer plenty to eat, too—they frequently reach a length of thirty inches, more rarely three feet.

The snakehead is a tough, resourceful fish, and its undershot jaw makes it appear as tough as it really is. With its capacious, strong-jawed mouth it attacks and feeds upon a wide variety of living creatures, including fishes, frogs, snakes, and insects. Its stocky but elongated body is wriggled snake-fashion, when the fish progresses over the ground. If the skin and breathing apparatus—which consists of a pair of chambers well supplied with blood vessels and located above the gill cavities—are kept moist, snakeheads can live out of water for a number of months, depending on their stored fat for food.

In preparation for spawning, an area in shallow water is cleared of vegetation. The eggs are amber coloured and about one-sixteenth of an inch in diameter. They float at the surface, hatching in about three days. The male guards both the eggs and the young fish. The latter remain at the surface for a day, then make periodic trips to the bottom for about another month before they take up life permanently at or near the bottom, coming to the top regularly to take a gulp of air and occasionally to snap up some unsuspecting animal there.

Although they are usually valuable as a source of food, snakeheads are pests in some places. Once they have got into a pond of fishes they proceed to destroy all of them and, having done so, move overland to another body of water. In India, fish culturists have to erect small fences around their fish ponds to keep marauding snakeheads out. A Formosan species was introduced into Japan and has proved most harmful to the native fishes.

Butterfly Fishes and Angel Fishes

THE SALT-WATER butterfly fishes and their relatives are among the brightest, most strikingly coloured of all fishes. Indeed, they seem to be aquatic copies of the lovely insects after which they were named. It is in coastal waters and around coral reefs that we are apt to encounter these fishes.

Wide from back to belly, and narrow from side to side, they are covered with small scales which extend on to the dorsal, anal, and tail fins. They have well-developed spines in the fins, and the ventral fins are located under or slightly in front of the pectorals.

These flat-bodied creatures have only a small mouth, and usually the teeth bear several cusps, being tiny and bristle-like in many instances—hence their scientific name, Order Chaetodontoidei, which means "spiny toothed". When small, the young usually pass through a peculiar stage: the head is armed with bony plates. There are well over two hundred different species; the majority dwell in the East and West Indies and around other tropical islands, one or two species venturing into brackish water.

The butterfly fishes (family Chaetodontidae) and the angel fishes (family Pomacanthidae) are the typical members of the order and include the vast majority of the species. The angel fishes are generally larger, reaching two feet in length. They are used for food in certain places.

We must travel to the far side of the world to meet some other members of this order. The scats (they make up the family Scatophagidae) regularly live in brackish and fresh water as well as salt, from the Red Sea through the Indian and western Pacific oceans as far north as Japan, as far south as Australia. The largest of the eight species attain a length of about one foot. In the more tropical part of their range we find their exotic relatives, the Moorish idols. The stout beak, the long, scimitar-shaped dorsal fin, and bold, vertical black, yellow, and white bands quickly distinguish them from all other fishes. There are only two species of these bright-hued creatures (family Zanclidae). The spadefishes (they form the family Ephippidae) occur in shallow, tropical, and warm-temperate seas, in the western Atlantic, with two or three in the eastern Pacific and one in the Indo-Pacific region. There are two or three other small families of Indo-Pacific fishes in this order.

The Foureye Butterfly Fish, *Chaetodon capistratus,* frequents coral reefs and adjacent areas from Panama to Florida and Bermuda. Strays are occasionally found as far north as Massachusetts; these are almost always young specimens that have been carried there by the Gulf Stream.

Strongly contrasted with the delicate yellow of this fish is the black band running vertically through its eye, the black eye itself, and the large black spot just beneath the rear portion of the dorsal fin. The latter, of course, is what gives the fish its name. Young individuals have a broad dusky area instead of this spot. A length of six inches is attained.

The Spadefish, *Chaetodipterus faber,* has a deep body that is quite narrow from side to side, being very similar to the angel fishes in this

[13-3]

The three and one-half inch salt-water clownfish has wide distribution from India through the East Indies to Queensland, the Philippines and other Pacific islands. Throughout most of this range it lives in very close co-operation with the giant sea anemone which, with this notable exception, is sudden death to small fish venturing within its reach. The clownfish flees to the aneome for protection, and lays its eggs where the stinging tentacles of its strange companion can be directed to cover the nest site. In return, the clownfish brings succulent titbits to the plantlike, voracious anemone, and expands and massages its tentacles. Nature being what it is, the clownfish occasionally eats the anemone.   *See page 1572*

[13-3A]

Of the more than 500 species of blennies, none is fully scaled and some lack scales altogether, hence the scientific name Blennoidei ("slimy") for these slippery fish. The fact that they are commonly known by a diminutive of their scientific name is an indication of the general lack of familiarity with the large group of hard-to-define fishes, in spite of the fact they are found almost everywhere —the warm, cold, shallow, deep, salt and fresh waters of the world play host to various members of this elusive clan. A few species leave the water of their own accord and spend almost half their time hopping about on rocks and reefs. Blennies proper prefer the shallow, tide-water pools of the warmer regions of the Western Hemisphere.   *See page 1584*

The blue marlin with its shining, dark blue back and silvery belly is one of the most beautiful of all the big-game fishes, its powerful, streamlined body being a delight to sportsmen and artists alike. The average weight of these fighting, swift-running, plunging, tail-dancing fish is around 200 pounds, but one 1,200-pound giant was reported caught in a net by Cuban fishermen, and the record rod-and-reel catch is an almost 13-foot specimen weighing just under 750 pounds. The blue marlin ranges the Atlantic Ocean for Montauk Point, Long Island, to Florida and the West Indies. Smaller species of marlin are found along the Atlantic Coast, off the shores of southern California, and in the South Pacific from Peru to New Zealand. All are much-sought-after gamefish. *See page 1595*

[13-4]

[13-4A]

Giant tunas are the largest of the bony fishes, and while the yellowfin tunas of the Pacific Ocean are not the most sizable of the sleek, spindle-shaped heavyweights, they constitute about two-thirds of the more than 200 million pounds of tuna taken each year. Yellowfins are believed to reproduce during the summer off the west coast of Central America and near the Philippine, Caroline and Marshall Islands; curiously enough large schools have recently been found in the Gulf of Mexico. The larger Atlantic bluefin breeds in and near the western Mediterranean, and history records the fact that tuna was a favourite food of the ancient Greeks and Romans.

See page 1591

[13-5]

The 300 known species of sculpins vary as much as in their choice of habitat as the blennies, although sculpins avoid the warmer waters. The freshwater varieties of Europe, North America and Asia seldom reach six inches in length but their salt-water cousins of the North Atlantic and Pacific and the Arctic Oceans may grow over two feet long. A large cabezon of the North Pacific may measure thirty inches and weigh twenty-five pounds. The cabezon is a typical bottom-dwelling member of the sculpin family, its rough, spiny skin blending with the rocky floor of the fairly shallow water it inhabits.   See page 1605

A number of peculiar fishes are classified together because they have armoured cheeks—bony plates or rods extending from the eyes back into the gill covers. Sculpins belong in this category, as does the bizarre, beautiful and poisonous zebra fish. Each ray or spine of the zebra's large dorsal and pectoral fins is separate, covered with its own narrow strip of fin, and is equipped with a poison gland. This native of the Indian Ocean and South-west Pacific has been known to eat itself to death—apparently not too difficult a feat, since the apparition-like waving fins seem to exert an immobilizing effect on the smaller fish on which the zebra preys.
See page 1607   [13-5A]

The more than 600 kinds of flat-fishes — flounders, plaice, sole, halibut, turbots and other less familiar species — begin life as "normal" fish but at a very early stage they turn on their sides and spend the rest of their lives swimming in a plane more or less parallel to the ocean floor. The remarkable thing is that their eyes move so that both are either on the right or left side, depending on the species, and other organs also shift. The starry flounder of the Pacific Ocean is a familiar and important game and foodfish from southern California to Alaska, and is also well known in Japan. Young starry flounders sometimes venture up streams to fresh water beyond the tide limits, but the adults are usually found in shallow water along the shore.

See page 1613

[13-6]

[13-6A]

The American plaice or sand dab averages only about seven pounds in comparison with the starry flounder's fifteen or twenty, but it is also an important foodfish, some three million pounds being taken annually. Dabs prefer the deeper water and are often found on muddy or sandy bottoms at depths of six hundred feet. Along with the other changes flatfishes undergo, the pigment of most species moves to the top or "eyed" side and the "blind" side becomes plain white; they all have the ability to change their coloration to blend with their surroundings. A few species of sole live in fresh water, but the vast majority of flatfishes are distributed throughout the oceans of the world from the Arctic almost to the Antarctic. See page 1613 regard. It has, however, two dorsal fins and these immediately distinguish it from them. Its coloration ranges from almost white to almost black, but usually consists of about five black vertical bars on a silvery grey background.

Spadefish have been taken along the Atlantic coast from Cape Cod to southern Brazil. They are only summer visitors north of Florida, and north of Chesapeake Bay they are rare at any time. The only exception to this is Bermuda, into whose warm waters spadefish have been introduced by man, and where they live all the year round. Spadefish are regularly used for food, but do not usually enter markets north of Panama. They reach a length of three feet and a weight of ten pounds.

The one-sixteenth-inch buoyant eggs are laid during late spring and summer. Hatching occurs in one day at 80° Fahrenheit, and the newly hatched young are a little less than one-eighth of an inch long. When less than an inch long, they are jet-black with completely transparent fins and they deceptively resemble the blackened pods of mangrove trees that are present in the water in some places at the same time the young spadefish are. This resemblance is greatly enhanced by the behaviour of the fish, which allow themselves to be rolled in gentle surf just as the inert pods are moved about by the ebbing and flowing water.

Surgeon Fishes: Creatures with Dangerous Tails

THE SURGEON, or doctor, fishes and the tangs carry curious weapons, to which they owe their names. On each side of the base of the tail they bear a sharp spine. These spines are shaped like a surgeon's lancet, and the fish can point them forward and outward, to gash or

maim other fishes as it swims by. Appropriately enough, the order is
known as Acanthuroidei ("spiny tails"). However, in some species the
spines are replaced by flat, bony plates.

Not quite one hundred species are known; they are found in tropical
seas, frequently around reefs. All belong to the family Acanthuridae.
Some species are brilliantly coloured. A few have a grotesque horn
growing straight forward out of the forehead, giving them the name
"unicorn fish". In fishes of this order the body is somewhat flattened
from side to side and is covered with fine scales. There are numerous
spines in the fins, and the pelvic fins are located well forward. The
teeth are chisel-like and the mouth small.

The Doctor Fish, *Acanthurus hepatus*, is equipped with a razor-
sharp spine on either side of the base of its tail fin. These lancet-like
structures can be raised and directed forward, in which position they
are formidable weapons. The fish inflicts deep wounds by coming along-
side another fish and side-swiping it as it passes by. Doctor fish can
also badly cut the hands of an incautious fisherman ignorant of its
hidden weapons.

This is a common fish in the West Indies and occurs south to Brazil.
North of Florida, with the exception of Bermuda, it exists only as
an occasional straggler. It reaches a length of about ten inches. It feeds
almost entirely on vegetable matter, mostly marine algae, having teeth
well developed for browsing. Swimming is largely accomplished by
"rowing" movements of the pectoral fins, the tail being used only in
times of stress.

The young are almost completely transparent, and drift with the
floating creatures of the surface of the sea. Depending on when they
are carried inshore, these larval fish, which may be only three-eighths
of an inch long at this time, leave their floating life and take up a more
or less bottom existence. At the same time they start to transform
into adult-like fish, completing the change in only two days.

Demoiselles and Cichlids
—Colourful and Clever

ANYONE who believes fish to be stupid creatures that just swim around, performing their life functions in a dull, uninteresting manner—whose only "cleverness" lies in their ability to escape the hook or net—should make the acquaintance of the remarkable demoiselles and cichlids of the order Chromides.

Here are fishes with complex and adaptable behaviour patterns that are truly amazing. Many of them show a sense of proprietorship, appropriating some underwater place as their very own. Their complicated courtships and the teamwork they use in bringing up their families remind one of animals like dogs or birds, usually thought to be much higher in the evolutionary scale. A few live in partnership with deadly sea anemones. It is fortunate that some of them can easily be kept in home aquaria, where their astonishing activities may be watched at first hand.

The demoiselles (family Pomacentridae) are small, tropical, saltwater fishes, in general brightly coloured, and usually inhabiting coral reefs and tide pools. So far as is known, their eggs are always guarded by at least one of the parents. The Beau-gregory, garibaldi and clownfish are demoiselles.

The cichlids (family Cichlidae) are tropical freshwater fishes, although several species spend a good deal of time in brackish water and a few can live for extended periods in sea water. Approximately six hundred species are known. In the Western Hemisphere, they are found from Texas south through Central America and most of South America and also on some islands of the West Indies. They are most numerous in Africa; for example, there are 178 different species in Lake Nyasa alone. Only two species occur in Asia, the chromides from southern India and Ceylon. The members of this family range in size up to nearly two feet, but most species grow to be less than half as long. Nearly one hundred kinds of cichlids have been imported into Europe and North America at one time or another as aquarium fishes for fish fanciers.

Our knowledge of the intricate reproductive behaviour of these fishes is based mostly on observations of captive specimens. Some kind of parental care is always in evidence. Frequently the male and female co-operate, both sharing—although sometimes unequally—in the tasks of preparing a site on which the eggs are laid, in guarding and cleaning the eggs, in transferring the hatching eggs or newly hatched young to specially prepared pits, in herding the young about, and in guarding them and putting them to bed in a pit at night. Sometimes the male alone assumes these responsibilities; in a few species, the female alone does so. A good deal of individuality is also shown, and the fish often modify their behaviour to meet the different situations they encounter.

The demoiselles and cichlids are distinguished from all other perch-like fishes by having a single nasal opening on each side of the snout —all other spiny-rayed fishes have two on each side. They also have characteristics of bony structure shared only with the Holoconti (sea perches) and Pharyngognathi (wrasses and parrot fishes).

The Beau-gregory, *Eupomacentrus leucostictus*, takes possession of a bit of territory at the bottom of the shallow sea or in some tide-pool and defends it against all comers, particularly other members of the same species. When a number of Beau-gregories are kept together in an aquarium, they kill one another off until the number of fish is such that each one is able to have a territory of its own. Only then does the killing cease.

In nature each territory usually includes some shell, nook, or cranny into which the Beau-gregory retires during the night and from which the fish sallies forth in daylight to feed or to chase away some intruder. During the breeding season, which extends from late spring throughout the summer, similar or identical places are employed as nests to shelter the eggs, which the male Beau-gregory guards and cleans with constant care.

Not only natural shelters—such as the shells of conchs and bivalves, or the under-surfaces of coral rocks and coral-like sea-fans—are utilized as nests, but a tin can, bottle or perhaps an abandoned shovel may provide some male with a home site. As many as four different female Beau-gregories may lay their eggs in the nest of a single male. The eggs are shaped like tiny, bright-yellow, gelatin capsules, about one thirty-second of an inch long, and are attached by one of their small ends to the shell, rock, etc., by a tuft of fine hairs. Hatching takes place in about five days, the larvae being somewhat less than one-eighth of an inch long.

Immature Beau-gregories have numerous bright blue spots on the forward part of the back; these are gradually lost as they grow up. The lower rear portion of the body is bright yellow. Adult males are generally larger than females, reaching about six inches, and they are more intensely coloured. In captivity their deep bluish-black and brilliant orange-yellow coloration fades quite a bit. It has been shown that this colour depends upon the fish's diet. If it does not obtain quantities of the algae upon which it naturally feeds, it loses its rich colours to some extent. Nevertheless, Beau-gregories seem to thrive on the unnatural, all-meat diet provided for them in aquariums.

An occasional Beau-gregory has straggled as far north as Maine, but the normal range of the species includes Bermuda, Florida and the West Indies.

The Garibaldi, *Hypsypops rubicunda,* has its entire body and all of its fins coloured a bright orange-red, only its black-and-cream eyes being different. Young ones, however, are entirely unlike adults; up to a size of about one and one-half inches they show numerous spots of scintillating blue, contrasting strongly with an orange or scarlet background. As they get older, the spots gradually disappear and the bright, background colour becomes dull and brownish, and by the time they are two inches long the fishes are quite drab in appearance. Finally, with the attainment of maturity, the characteristic bright colours develop.

Accompanying these decisive changes in colour are equally radical changes in behaviour. The very small, brightly coloured garibaldis live on rocky reefs where grow several species of algae which shine with a similar metallic blue. The dull, half-grown fish hide most of the time, in contrast to the brilliant adults who frequently display themselves, as if advertising their presence, over their home territories, which they defend staunchly against other fish, especially other garibaldis.

In general shape, the body of the garibaldi is similar to that of the sunfish—to which it is not at all closely related, however. The species grows to a length of about fourteen inches and is probably the largest member of its family. It is found around rocky shores on the Pacific coast of North America from Point Conception to northern Baja California. It feeds upon crustaceans and seaweed. Although they do well in aquariums, captive garibaldis generally lose their bright colour, and become a pale lemon-yellow.

The Clownfish, *Amphiprion percula*, lives in partnership with giant sea anemones. These creatures of the genera *Stoichactis* and *Discosoma* may have a diameter of sixteen to twenty-four inches, and are attached to the bottom by a fleshy base. At the centre is the mouth and surrounding this along the edges are hundreds of tentacles, armed with thousands of stinging cells. Woe betide any small fish coming too close to these deadly arms, for it is quickly stung to death and then carried to the anemone's mouth to be eaten.

Clownfish, however, live within the area surrounded by these tentacles with impunity. Although other fishes and small animals are killed by the anemones, when a clownfish darts among these sting-bearing tentacles, they curl away and do it no harm. Even when clownfish brush up against the tentacles, they are not stung. Whenever clownfish are alarmed, they flee to the protection of their anemone; they also apparently spend their nights amidst the tentacles.

The anemones also profit by this association. Whenever a clownfish comes upon a piece of food too large to be consumed on the spot, it brings the morsel to its anemone and usually shares the food with it. According to some observers, the clownfish also cleans the anemone, aerates it by circulating water around it, and makes the anemone expand by rubbing its tentacles, presumably improving its condition. On the other hand, clownfish occasionally feed upon their anemones to a limited extent.

Clownfish are widely distributed from India through the East Indies to Queensland, the Philippines and the islands of the Pacific. In most of these regions they have been seen associated with giant anemones, as many as seven clownfish being taken from a single anemone. Clownfish can exist perfectly well, however, without an anemone partner —in captivity at least, where their peculiar pattern of brilliant colours and their engaging ways have made them most popular. They reach a length of three and one-half inches, and are bright orange, with three white bands bordered in black running vertically across the back of the head, the middle of the body, and the base of the tail. The fins are bordered with white and black.

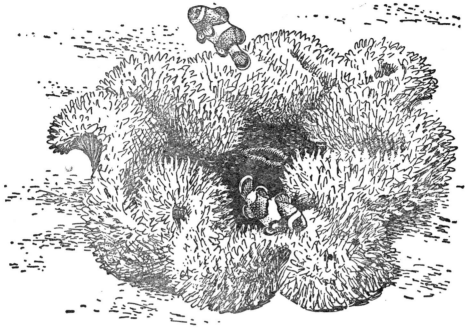

A STRANGE PARTNERSHIP

Clownfish are interesting little creatures, drolly costumed in orange, black, and white. Like the two pictured above, they make their home inside a creature known as the giant sea anemone, which looks like a plant but is actually an animal with poisonous tentacles. The clownfish share their food with the anemone in exchange for the safe shelter it affords them. Their eggs are also laid near the protecting anemone.

The nest of the clownfish is usually located very close to an anemone, and the fish may direct the stinging tentacles of its partner so that they cover the nest site. The spot is well cleaned and the peculiarly shaped eggs are attached to it in a single layer. The eggs are cylindrical in shape with rounded ends. Both parents co-operate in caring for their spawn, the male performing the greater part of the actual care of the eggs. For seven to ten days he watches over them, cleaning them with his mouth. Meanwhile the female, which may be twice as large as her mate, usually remains in the vicinity.

The newly hatched larvae travel to the water surface where they float with other creatures for about two weeks. At first they are about three-sixteenths of an inch long and grey in colour. Within two weeks they have started to assume the colour pattern of the adult, and at this time they drop to the bottom to search for an anemone of their own. Clownfish are quite prolific. One captive pair had sixteen broods within eight months. In nature, reproduction takes place during most of the year.

The Black-chinned Mouthbreeder, *Tilapia macrocephala*, leads a complicated home life of the kind usually associated with creatures much higher than fishes in the evolutionary scale. These fish pair off, the male and female courting each other by nodding their heads, puffing out their throats or quivering in view of each other, and by chasing, nipping, or slapping each other with their tails. The female courts more vigorously than does the male.

As time for spawning approaches a nest is constructed by scooping out a round or oval depression in the bottom and cleaning it most carefully. The female, too, is the more active nest-builder. Then the pair begins to swim over the nest, the female in front of the male, in what might for a while be called false spawning activity, and finally about fifty large eggs are laid and fertilized. These are not spherical but assume a variety of shapes, averaging somewhat more than one-sixteenth of an inch in their greatest dimension.

Soon after the eggs have been laid, the male approaches the nest and picks the eggs up with his mouth. If he delays in doing this, the female nips him violently and slaps him vigorously with her tail. In rare instances the male still refuses to take over his parental duties, and at last the female herself picks up the eggs. If the male is small, there may be too many eggs for his mouth, and the female will then take into hers those that are left over.

The eggs generally hatch in five days, but the young are carried in the parent's mouth from two to fifteen days longer. Once they have been released, the young are no longer cared for in any way. While carrying eggs or young, the parent fish does not feed, but more or less continuously churns its offspring about.

The black-chinned mouthbreeder is a native of tropical west Africa, where it inhabits both fresh and brackish waters, principally swamps and lagoons. It sometimes reaches a length of about twelve inches. Its general appearance is not indicative of any strange behaviour nor is its light olive coloration very striking. A series of irregular black spots around the head, especially the lower jaw, is responsible for its name.

Among the numerous species of cichlids that are mouthbreeders, several different patterns of behaviour are shown. In many *Tilapia*, the baby fish are released from the female's mouth to forage under her watchful care, returning to her mouth in times of disturbance and at night. This is also true of the large genus *Haplochromis*, of which the Egyptian mouthbreeder of home aquaria is a member. In certain South American cichlids, the eggs are apparently not carried in the mouth, although the young are. The male alone does the carrying.

THE BLACK-CHINNED MOUTHBREEDER—AN AFRICAN CURIOSITY

The black-chinned mouthbreeder hatches its eggs in its mouth. After these curious fish have scooped out a nest in the bottom, the female lays her eggs in it. Like the male shown here, the father must promptly pick them up in his mouth or else the female will buffet him soundly with her tail. For the one or two weeks the father carries his eggs about, he does not eat a single morsel of food.

The Scalare or Freshwater Angel Fish, *Pterophyllum eimekei,* is, next to the guppy, the best known of all the small tropical fishes kept as pets. Its stately appearance and unusual hardiness in captivity have made it a favourite with fanciers, and its responsiveness to expert care for regular breeding under controlled conditions has kept it popular with professional fish culturists. When scalares were first imported into

America, small ones sold for as much as ten dollars each, but they are now commercially bred in such large numbers that they are often priced as low as twenty-five cents.

Native to the Amazon Basin and the Guianas, scalares inhabit shallow, quiet streams and backwaters that are well supplied with aquatic vegetation. The fish reach lengths of five to six inches. They are quite narrow from side to side and quite deep from back to belly. The pectoral fins are each drawn out into a fine ray that may be half again as long as the fish itself, and the tail fin has a long ray at its top and bottom. These, and the high, sail-like dorsal fin, give the fish a most elegant appearance, which is not belied by its deliberate and graceful movements. The colour is silvery, with four vertical black bands.

The eggs of the scalare are laid on the leaves of aquatic plants or on the more or less vertical sides of stones. Both parents care for their eggs and young.

Sea-Perch—Spectacular Live-Bearing Fish

OFF THE Pacific coast of North America dwells an interesting and important group of fishes, the sea-perch. Every year, fishermen draw over one hundred tons of them from shallow waters, from Baja California to Alaska. We also find them in fairly deep sea water, and Chinese and Japanese fishermen look for them off their coasts. One species, too, lives in streams in California. So, although sea-perch are most at home in shallow coastal waters, we see that they have adapted themselves to varying places and conditions.

The most striking thing about the sea-perch is the way it bears its young. Unlike most other fishes, it brings its offspring into the world alive, not in the form of eggs. The mother fish may carry her unborn babies in her body quite a while, and they may be remarkably mature at birth. That is why scientists named this order Holoconti ("born whole"). Such young fishes have relatively few problems of survival.

An adult sea-perch may be five to eighteen inches in length, depending on its species. (There are twenty-five in the family Embiotocidae, which makes up the order.) The lips are thick and fleshy. Pelvic fins are close behind the pectorals, and some of the fins have spines. A good help in identification is the furrow on each side of the base of the dorsal fin.

The Shiner Sea-perch, *Cymatogaster aggregatus,* brings forth its young alive—and in such an advanced condition that within two days of birth the young males are courting females and mating with them. In other words, baby male shiner sea-perch are already sexually mature when born! This has been proved not only by their obviously adult behaviour, but also by microscopic examination of their sex glands, which shows that they are in a condition comparable with those in large, old males.

Shiner sea-perch are quite ordinary-appearing fish with compressed, elliptical bodies and rather fleshy lips. They are predominantly silver in colour, darker on the back than on the belly. Males are almost black during the winter and spring. They are smaller than the females, reaching a length of not quite five inches, while females exceed six inches occasionally. If the anal fin of the male is examined closely, the small, masculine genital organ can be seen at the anterior edge.

From April to July, shiner sea-perch appear in shallow waters from southern California to Alaska both to deliver their young and to mate for the next year's offspring. The eggs within the female are not fertilized until midwinter, however; the male sexual secretion remains dormant within the female's reproductive tract until that time. The eggs are extremely minute, being slightly more than one one-hundredth of an inch in diameter. Yet these tiny eggs develop into baby fish that are more than one and one-quarter inches long at birth. This great increase in size is made possible by the feeding of the developing embryo within the mother's ovary. The embryonic fish at first feed through a gill-opening by means of microscopic, hair-like cilia that produce a current by rhythmically waving, and carry down into the embryo's digestive tract the more or less liquid nourishment in which the developing fish floats. This nourishment is provided by the walls of the ovary, which secrete a special substance and which also periodically shed part of themselves into the ovarian fluid. The specially produced liquid, the part of the ovarian walls shed into it, and excess sperm are all consumed by the embryonic shiner sea-perch.

For five to six months the fish grow inside their mother. As they get larger they become packed quite tightly within the ovary. A six-inch female usually has about sixteen offspring in a brood, each of which is about one-sixth as long as she is. As many as thirty-six young have been counted in a single litter, however. Newly born females are not as well developed as males; nevertheless they give birth to their first brood when just one year old.

The food of the shiner sea-perch consists principally of small crustaceans and other invertebrates.

Several other species of sea-perch are more important economically than is the shiner sea-perch. A goodly number of the latter are brought to market, however. In all, about three hundred thousand pounds of various sea-perch are caught commercially each year in the United States, while several species are popular anglers' fishes.

Wrasses and Parrot Fishes
—Dwellers of the Coral Reefs

IT IS in the warm waters of tropical seas around the world that we are most likely to find the gorgeously coloured creatures known as wrasses and parrot fishes. Here they swarm around coral reefs and gather in large numbers in coastal areas. Strange, vivid fishes, they are among the most flamboyant yet beautiful of things that live in the water.

It is no easy matter to observe the ways of the wrasses and parrot fishes in these faraway places, and many of their habits still remain an unopened book to us. If we could watch these dwellers of the coral reefs up close, we would see some fascinating happenings, however. For example, we might behold some of the razor fishes—a kind of wrasse—building cone-shaped mounds of coral fragments with a central crater in which they would later bury themselves to hide from enemies. Perhaps they use these retreats as nests, too, but we are not sure.

We might, too, see other wrasses patiently wedging seaweed into rocky crevices. This is no aimless activity—the fishes are actually building nests to lay their eggs in. The eggs of these species are heavier than sea water, and the nest helps to assure their safety. Some wrasses and parrot fishes lay lighter eggs, and these float buoyantly on the surface of the sea.

The fishes in this order feed on molluscs and other hard-shelled creatures, as well as the plant life they find in their native waters. Such a diet is not an easy one to swallow, but the wrasses and parrot fishes are strikingly equipped for the task. In their throats they have an efficient natural mill. The throat bones are fused together, and out of them, both at the top and bottom of the gullet, there usually grows a series of pavement-like or hemispherical teeth that serve to grind the food. (The order name—Pharyngognathi—means "throat-jaws".) The jaw teeth are also strong and prominent. In the parrot fishes they are more or less grown together, often to form a distinctly parrot-like beak, from which these fishes get their name. The fins are well spined and the pelvic fins have a rather forward position.

Some of the wrasses are at home in quite cold ocean waters, and in both tropical and temperate regions they are caught for food. Most species (there are about 450, forming the family Labridae) do not exceed one foot in size, but a few attain lengths of more than two feet and one reaches more than seven feet. Among the better-known wrasses are the tautog, cunner, hogfish, California sheepshead, pudding wife, señorita, bluehead, and razor fishes. Sometimes males and females are strikingly different in colour pattern and shape. The parrot fishes (there are more than one hundred species in the family Scaridae) range in size up to about four feet.

The Tautog, *Tautoga onitis,* feeds chiefly on shellfish, especially mussels, clams, and barnacles. It has two types of teeth, conical and flat; the former are used in holding and tearing prey, the latter in crushing it. The tautog is a stocky fish with an arched forehead, thick lips and an extremely deep base to the tail fin. The single dorsal and anal fins are well spined. Its colour is very dark green, grey, or black.

The range of the tautog is along the Atlantic coast of North America from New Brunswick to South Carolina. Reproduction takes place in the early summer. The small eggs are buoyant and hatch in two days at about 70 degrees. The record fish weighed 22½ pounds and was 36½ inches long, but any individual over ten pounds is unusual.

The Bluehead or King Slippery Dick, *Thalassoma bifasciatum*, undergoes a remarkable series of colour changes as it grows up. How puzzling this has proved to scientists you can well imagine. Young fish less than half an inch long have a wide dark brown band that extends from the snout through the eye to the tail fin. Above this band the slender body is generally pale green; below, it is white somewhat tinged with pink. No problem so far—but as the fish get larger, males and females become more and more unalike.

In the females, the band breaks up into a series of blotches, and the lower portion of the body becomes a pale blue with a pinkish tinge. The males pass through several stages, eventually exhibiting a deep blue or greenish head, separated from a bottle-green body by two wide, irregular, black bars that run from the dorsal to the ventral fins, just behind the pectorals. Between these two black bars the body is pale blue. The tail of the male develops an extension at its upper and lower edges, making it appear as if a semicircle had been cut out of the rear.

So different are all the various stages that they were once thought to be different species of fishes. Not until large series of specimens of successive sizes were available for study, and the actual changes had been witnessed in fish growing up in aquaria, was the confusing situation straightened out. To make things even more complicated, males sometimes assume female coloration and there are some medium-sized individuals that are predominantly yellow. At night a different colour pattern is assumed, but the bluehead does not try to match its surroundings by altering its colour scheme.

Blueheads are found around Florida and Bermuda and in the West Indies. During the day they actively swim about coral reefs and other underwater growths, often in small groups. Apparently they feed principally on small crustaceans. Young specimens are sometimes seen pecking at the bodies of larger fishes, which do not seem to mind this attention. It has been thought that the small blueheads were picking parasites off the other fish, but no parasite has ever been found in their stomachs.

At night blueheads hide in shells or bury themselves in the sand. Spawning takes place in the summer. The eggs are very small and float on the surface of the open sea. Blueheads reach a size of six inches.

The Blue Parrot Fish, *Scarus coeruleus,* is usually coloured a robin's-egg blue and so brilliant is this pigment that the fish seems to shine through its large scales as if luminescent. Sometimes it shows darker stripes or blotches, and rarely it becomes very pale throughout. It reaches a length of about three feet.

Blue parrot fish straggle as far north as Maryland, but are not at all common north of Florida except around Bermuda. They range as far south as Panama. During the day most of their time is spent in feeding; they browse on the bottom, eating algae and other marine growths, which they remove in a dainty fashion yet with considerable force by means of their sharp, beaklike teeth. They sometimes take up mouthfuls of fine sand, swallowing it after chewing it with their throat teeth, presumably to obtain very small bits of organic material. Vegetable matter appears essential to their diet—they will not live long in captivity unless they have some to feed upon. At the New York Aquarium, they consumed sea-lettuce, *Ulva,* with seeming relish.

The Radiant Parrot Fish, *Sparisoma radians,* has a most variable coloration. In addition, the male is differently coloured from the female. Consequently this fish has been described as a new species no less than seven different times by scientists who did not know that the specimen or specimens they had in hand were merely colour or sexual variants.

The male also differs from the female in possessing lateral canine teeth (fangs) when only two inches long, while the female does not grow them until almost three inches long. At this size the females are mature. They lay pelagic eggs (floating on the open sea) during the summer. Specimens nine inches long have been reported. Their range includes Bermuda, Florida, and the West Indies, south to Brazil.

The Lesser Weever, *Trachinus vipera,* conceals itself in the sand in shallow waters from the Mediterranean to the British Isles. These small fish, reaching a length of about five inches, are equipped with a single, long, needle-sharp spine on each gill-cover and with five smaller spines in the first dorsal fin, all of which have poison glands at their bases. Anyone unfortunate enough to tread on a lesser weever, or foolish enough to handle one carelessly, suffers agonizing pain when pricked by these poisonous spines. Such cases often require hospital treatment, and recovery from the injury is a tedious and rather painful process.

The spawning season of the lesser weever is from May to September. Their buoyant eggs are about one-sixteenth of an inch in diameter. Hatching occurs in about ten days, and the larvae float at the surface of the sea for some time before settling to the bottom to take up an adult-like existence. They feed on small crustaceans and fishes.

The weevers, of which less than half a dozen species are known, make up the family Trachinidae which belongs to the order Trachinoidea. They are found in the eastern Atlantic Ocean and in the Mediterranean Sea. It is believed that they are related to the stargazers.

The Northern Electric Stargazer, *Astroscopus guttatus*, buries itself in sand at the bottom of coastal waters off the eastern shore of the United States, from New York to Virginia. Its eyes are located on the flattened top of its head and look directly upward. Its large mouth is practically vertical, the tip being at the same level as, and just in front of, the eyes. When the stargazer is covered with sand, only its minute eyes are visible. From this hidden position, it makes short dashes to catch unwary fishes passing by; it then settles back on the bottom, and, with a few wriggles of its body and pectoral fins, it is again perfectly concealed—all within the span of a few seconds.

Just behind each eye is an oval, bare spot; this is the site of the upper end of a column of electric tissue which extends down through the head to the roof of the mouth. The electric shock from these organs cannot compare with that of the electric eel or the torpedoes in strength, but when the fish is handled, it can be readily felt. Its voltage has not yet been measured; in fact all that seems to be known about the electric stargazer's discharge is that the top of the head is negative, the bottom positive, and that it is under the voluntary control of the fish. Whether or not the fish ever uses its electricity to obtain food is unknown, although what evidence there is indicates

[13-7]

The scales of the cowfish's head and body have become modified into hexagonal plates securely cemented together to form a hard, immovable case. The fins, eyes, jaws and tail project through this rigid shell, and the cowfish "sculls" or "rows" itself through the water at a rather slow pace. They range on both sides of the tropical Atlantic, feeding on worms and other small creatures that live in coral reef formations; they can easily crack the stone with their sharp, powerful teeth. Adult cowfish reach a length of about one foot, and while they may not look appetizing, their flesh is generally considered delicious; they are often cooked in their own shells.

See page 1625

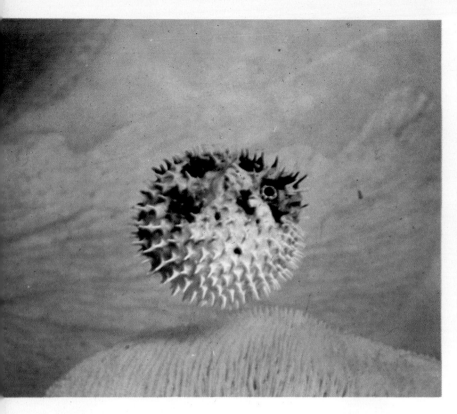

The life history of the porcupine fish is somewhat of a mystery, although it is found in tropical seas the world over and is well known to many peoples. A member of the puffer family, this fish is covered with numerous long, sharp spines which ordinarily lie close to its body but which stick straight out when the fish inflates itself. Porcupine fish grow to a length of more than three feet, the inflated larger specimens resembling nail-studded basketballs. The Japanese use it for food although it is considered poisonous in most countries; the flesh may become toxic by absorbing poison from the fish's vital organs after its death.

See page 1629

[13-8]

Against a background of the sargassum weed in which it lives and from which it takes its name, this fish disappears before one's eyes. The pectoral fins are so constructed that the sargassum fish can actually grasp a branch of the floating seaweed and hold on to it. It swims slowly in mid-water, utilizing the jets of water emitted from its gill openings, and is capable of making relatively great flying leaps. With enormous mouths and stomachs that can be stretched out of all proportion to their size, the four-inch sargassums can swallow fish larger than themselves. Found in practically all tropical seas, sargassum fish occasionally drift north with the seaweed.

See page 1637

[13-8A]

that it is only employed defensively. The electric organs are derived from parts of the fish's eye muscles.

Another peculiarity of the electric stargazer is that its nostrils open into the mouth, enabling it to breathe water through them while hidden under sand. (The noses of the vast majority of living fishes consist of U-shaped sacs which open only to the exterior and are used for smelling, not for breathing.) This species reaches a length of twenty-two inches and a weight of about twenty pounds. Eggs that float are laid during the late spring. At first the young also float about, but by autumn, when they have grown to be somewhat more than an inch long, they have taken up life on the bottom.

Not all the stargazers, which comprise the family Uranoscopidae, possess electric organs; only a few of them are so equipped. Less than twenty-five species of stargazers are known, but they inhabit most tropical and warm-temperate seas. All of them live at the bottom; a few, in considerable depths. The largest species slightly exceed two feet in length.

The European Stargazer, *Uranoscopus scaber*, possesses a fleshy, frilled filament, which can be extended out of its mouth and wiggled about, simulating the motions of a small, red worm. Lying concealed in sand or mud, this stargazer is able to lure other fishes within reach of its capacious jaws. Like other members of its family, the European stargazer lays eggs that float on the open sea. These eggs are about one-sixteenth of an inch in diameter, and are spawned at night during the late spring and summer. This species is found in the warm parts of the eastern Atlantic and in the Mediterranean. It attains a length of about thirteen inches.

Blennies—Some Are Wolf-fishes

WHAT BLENNIES lack in size and popularity, they make up in oddity and interest. The more we learn about them—and there is still a tremendous lot we do not know—the more fascinating they become. For example, some of the blennies seem as much at home on land as they do in the water! A few of these little creatures spend almost half their time hopping about on rocks and reefs. They are not washed up there by rough seas, either—they leave the water of their own free will.

Most of the blennies proper (family Blenniidae) are small fishes less than six inches long. They love shallow, warm salt waters. Here, among the rocks and seaweeds of shores, tide pools, reefs and inlets, they hide from enemies on the prowl. Only relatively few dwell in cold or fresh waters.

In crevices or under shells and other submerged objects, the female blenny lays her eggs. These, so far as we know, are adhesive. In many species the male stands guard over them. Often you can tell him apart from the female—differences in the colour and shape of the sexes are fairly common.

The kelpfishes or klipfishes (family Clinidae) remind us of the blennies proper in many ways. They, too, generally favour shallow salt waters, in tropical and temperate regions, and are often seen in tide pools among rocks and seaweed. Some are quite brightly hued, and males and females occasionally have a differently shaped body and fins. A number of species give birth to living young, and one kind—it is found in the West Indies—uses the inside of living sponges as a nursery. Kelpfishes are usually larger than the members of the preceding family, but seldom exceed one foot. The two groups, together, include perhaps five hundred species.

In the cold waters of the North Atlantic and Pacific live the savage-

1584

looking wolf-fishes (family Anarhichadidae). These blennies have powerful jaws armed with strong fangs in the front and heavy plates of rounded grinding teeth behind. Wolf-fishes they are in name and appearance, and their disposition seems to be fearless as well. But they use their formidable biting and chewing equipment not so much to prey upon other fish as they do to rake up and crush the hard-shelled molluscs upon which they frequently feed.

By and large, the wolf-fishes are giants compared to the other blennies we have been talking about. The common Atlantic wolf-fish averages about three feet in length. The eastern Pacific breeds a super-giant, a very elongated creature that reaches eight feet. For the way it cares for its young, the wolf-fish of the Atlantic is especially interesting to us. It spawns large eggs which are then formed into a ball. One of the parents stands guard over it to keep it from harm.

Of the several other families of cold-water blennies only the eel-pouts of the cold seas of the Northern and Southern Hemispheres are of any economic importance. Some species lay eggs, others give birth to live young.

As a group, the blennies and their many relatives are difficult to define. They do have one or two bony features in common, but we cannot see these from the outside. The ventral fins, if there are any, are far forward, just in front of the pectorals. These fins have either a single spine followed by up to four fin rays, or just this small number of rays without any spine. The body, rather elongated, sometimes reminds us of an eel's. The dorsal fin usually extends the full length of the back, but may be shorter. The blenny's anal fin, too, is long, extending over much of its under-side. Spines may or may not be present in these two fins. Some species lack scales; none is fully scaled, and thus the blenny is a rather slippery fish. Accordingly the order to which it belongs is called Blennoidei ("slimy"). There are about eighteen families in all.

The American Eelpout, *Macrozoarces americanus,* is one of the many fishes, generally considered to be "trash" species in the commercial fisheries of the Atlantic coast of the United States, that in reality are excellent foodfish which could provide many people with nutritious, tasty, yet economical fare—if only the prejudice against their use could be overcome. Some progress in the education of the consuming public along these lines has been made; for example, four million pounds of eelpouts were marketed during the war years, 1943 and 1944. One cannot overestimate the importance of this kind of development in conserving strained natural resources.

The appearance of the eelpout is undoubtedly the principal reason it is unpopular. It is an ugly fish with a heavy head, a large mouth surrounded by thick lips and a long, tapering body. The long dorsal fin is continuous with the tail fin, which in turn is continuous with the long anal. The coloration of the eelpout is variable but sombre.

This bottom-dwelling fish ranges from Labrador and Newfoundland to Delaware, and from shallow waters to those of considerable depth. It feeds principally on crustaceans and molluscs. Maximum length is three and one-half feet and maximum weight about twelve pounds, but specimens over three feet are rare.

Reproduction is by means of large, heavy eggs about one-quarter of an inch in diameter. These are laid during the late summer and autumn down into crevices or other protected places, and are there guarded by one or both parents. From two and one-half to three and one-half months elapse before hatching, depending on the temperature. A close relative of the eelpout from Europe, *Zoarces viviparus*, gives birth to living young.

Brotulids, Cusk-Eels and Pearlfishes —Little-Known Oddities

MOST OF us have never even heard of these fishes, but they deserve to be known because of their extremely curious ways of life. Some of the most remarkable of the group are the brotulids (family Brotulidae). Although the greater number are at home in the deep sea, a few strange species live out their lives in the darkness of freshwater caves in Cuba and Yucatan. We call these cave-dwellers "blind-fish", for they have only the slightest traces of eyes. Still, they have managed to make up for their lack of sight: they have developed tiny growths or barbels on their heads to serve as "feelers". Thus the blind species are perfectly at ease in the pitch-black underground waters, where eyes would be of no use to them anyway. They give birth to living young, as do some, if not all, of their ocean-going relatives.

Equally fascinating are a group of small, eel-shaped creatures, the pearlfishes (family Fierasferidae). The pearlfish often makes its home inside the shell of the pearl oyster or some other living mollusc, or it may take up quarters in some other animal—the hind-gut of a live sea-cucumber or a starfish is not an unlikely place to find a pearlfish. From time to time it leaves this strange shelter to search for food or to lay its floating eggs. Not all pearlfishes live in other creatures, and many prefer to haunt rocky crevices. Almost every shallow, tropical sea is the dwelling place of some of these little oddities.

Because they are built on the general lines of the eel, the next family we shall turn our attention to is known as the cusk-eels (Ophidiidae). One, a five-foot giant that snakes through the waters off South Africa and Australia, is a good catch for any fisherman, being esteemed as a foodfish. Most, though, are under a foot long. They are deep-water fishes of the warm seas, as a rule.

What obvious features, then, do the fishes of this order—Ophidioidei ("snakelike")—have in common? Generally, their resemblance to the eels is the one that strikes us strongly. Their bodies are quite elongated, and the scales are tiny or absent altogether. Usually there is no tail fin, and the other fins lack spines. The ventral fins, if present at all, are located far forward and reduced to a few rays.

Mackerel, Tuna, and Their Relatives —Mighty, Far-Ranging Swimmers

POWERFUL, far-ranging swimmers with streamlined bodies that cut through the ocean waters at great speeds—such are the mackerel, the tuna, the swordfish, and most of their relatives. Because their flesh is savoury and rich in oil, and because they frequently travel about in schools—and therefore can be easily caught in large numbers—several species have become extremely important foodfishes. Some put up a staunch fight in the catching, and are highly prized as game-fishes.

The mackerel is typical of its family (Scombridae), which includes the bonito, tuna, albacore, and skipjack. With pointed head and spindle-shaped body, it is superbly contoured for sliding through the ocean with the ease of a torpedo. Like the rest of its family, which contains about fifty species, it makes its home in all the temperate and tropical seas of the earth. Only in warmer seas do we find the Spanish mackerel and its strangely named relative the wahoo, a dark-blue denizen of the waters off Florida and the West Indies. These belong to a separate family (Scomberomoridae) which contains about a dozen different fishes, ranging up to six feet and one hundred pounds in size.

The escolars were "scholars" to the Spaniards, who named them that because the species they pulled from the water had circles around their eyes, reminding the fishermen of glasses. These large, voracious fishes (family Gempylidae) dwell in open temperate and tropical seas, sometimes being found at considerable depths. Best known is the Barracouta, or Snoek, *Thyrsites atun*, which is one of the two most important commercial fishes of Australia, and is also widely used for food in South Africa. It lives only in the cooler ocean waters of the Southern Hemisphere, and reaches a length of three and one-half feet.

Like the great barracuda, with which it should not be confused, it can inflict terrible wounds with its fangs and numerous smaller teeth. It has never been known to attack bathers in water, however.

Another interesting group in this order includes such curiosities as cutlass fishes and scabbard fishes. These sharp-toothed creatures have elongated bodies that reach a length of at least five feet, and bear a striking resemblance to the objects for which they are named. Some species have no tail fin at all, and the end of the fish tapers to a point so fine that it looks like a hair. It is not surprising that the scientific name given them should mean just that—"hair-tails" (family Trichiuridae). In India they are fished on a commercial scale.

We find a number of other famous fishes in this imposing order: the broadbill swordfish, the spearfish, and the various marlins and sailfishes. About some of these we shall have much to say later.

The order—Scombroidei ("mackerel-like")—has perhaps a dozen families, all told. Although related to the spiny-rayed fishes, they do not always have spines in their fins. The ventral fins, if present, are usually found well forward. A series of small fins, called finlets, frequently runs from the dorsal and from the anal to the tail fin. The attachment of the tail fin to the body is usually slender, with a horizontal keel on either side. If the fish has any scales at all, they are small and we cannot easily see or feel them. The structure of the pointed mouth, which cannot be extended, helps us to identify members of the order.

The Atlantic Mackerel, *Scomber scombrus,* provides Americans with about thirty-five million pounds of fish each year, although the amount caught varies widely, some years being "good mackerel years", others bad ones. The reason for these fluctuations is unknown, but it is suspected that excessive mortality of very young mackerel may be responsible. Unfavourable winds that blow the more or less helpless, floating baby fish into unsuitable waters, or a lack of the proper microscopic or near-microscopic plants and animals to feed them are two factors that may cause mass mortality.

In the western Atlantic, spawning of the mackerel takes place about twenty miles offshore from April into June. The numerous eggs float near the surface and hatch in about a week, but the young fish are not capable of swimming effectively for almost a month, being pretty much at the mercy of the elements during this period.

Even when lying limply on ice in a fish store, the mackerel appears graceful, but its streamlined form cannot be really appreciated save in action—when the fish courses through the water, powered by rhythmical strokes of its muscular tail, the dark network on the blue-green of its back adding to the illusion of some sort of aquatic rocket or bullet.

FISH THAT SWIM FOR THEIR LIVES

Most animals may pause and rest sometime, but not the adult Atlantic mackerel—if it stops swimming, it will suffocate, for it requires a continuous flow of fresh water to keep its blood supplied with oxygen. By day mackerel travel in schools that often number thousands, but on dark nights these schools break up.

From the time they are about two inches long and forty days old and have assumed the shape of the adult, Atlantic mackerel swim continuously until they die. In fact, if a mackerel stops swimming, it *will* die, being smothered because not enough water passes over its gills. If possible, mackerel remain in the company of thousands of their fellows, more or less of the same size and all moving at the same speed and in the same direction. These great oceanic schools break up at night unless there is a moon, and do not re-form until dawn. Experiments have shown that fish will not school unless they can see one another. Blinded mackerel in the dark pay no attention to their fellow fish, but two mackerel placed in separate tanks, close together, will school with each other, swimming side by side, back and forth along the glass sides of the tanks.

While moving about, Atlantic mackerel feed voraciously on practically all kinds of floating animals, including shrimps, worms, squid, fish eggs and fry, small adult fishes, and even small mackerel. During certain parts of the year they live on bivalves and other bottom-inhabiting creatures. The ordinary Atlantic mackerel is about one foot long and weighs about one pound. Specimens more than twice as long, weighing seven and one-half pounds, are on record, however.

In the western Atlantic, this species ranges from Labrador to North Carolina. During the spring, summer, and autumn, the fish remain near the surface, but in winter they move farther offshore and sink down, possibly as deep as one hundred fathoms.

The Pacific Mackerel, *Pneumatophorus diego,* is caught in larger numbers than the Atlantic mackerel, but it, too, is subject to wide fluctuations. Almost all of the Pacific mackerel caught are canned, rather than sold fresh or frozen as is the Atlantic species. It averages somewhat larger than the Atlantic species, but does not attain quite so large a maximum size. Although the Pacific mackerel looks quite like its Atlantic relative, it can be clearly separated from it by the possession of an air bladder and several other structural details. Both species have their bodies covered with very fine scales.

Spawning occurs from late April through July along the California coast. Floating on the open sea, the eggs hatch in about three days. The Pacific mackerel is a schooling species and feeds on various floating crustaceans, on squid, and on small fishes.

The Bluefin Tuna, *Thunnus thynnus,* has a sleek, spindle-shaped body that is beautifully fashioned for slipping through water with a minimum of effort. No protuberance or lack of symmetry mars its streamlined contours. The jaws fit neatly together, and the gill covers lie close against the sides. The eyes are set flush with the surface of the head. Even the paired fins and the first dorsal fit into grooves, lest they present unnecessary water resistance. The scales are very small and buried within smooth skin that is as slippery as slime can make it.

Everything about the tuna indicates aquatic speed and a life of continuous swimming, and the fish certainly lives up to its appearance. Tuna have been clocked at speeds of more than forty miles per hour and they can apparently maintain rates of about nine miles per hour indefinitely. No one has ever seen a tuna that was not swimming, unless it was dead or dying. Using the above figures, it can be estimated that a fifteen-year-old tuna must have travelled in the order of a million miles during its life. The tuna is one of the very few fish that maintain a body temperature somewhat higher than that of the surrounding water, and without doubt this is closely associated with its continuous activity.

Travelling about in schools through most of the temperate and tropical seas, tuna have been likened to packs of wolves—so relentlessly do they pursue their prey and so ravenously do they feed upon it. Squid and fishes make up the bulk of their food.

Tuna were a favourite food of the ancient Greeks and Romans. Today they are fished both commercially and for sport in many parts of the world. In commercial fisheries they are netted, harpooned, trolled, or pole-fished with two or three poles to a single hook when the fish run large. Tuna fishing is now the most profitable of all of California's fisheries. Practically all of the catch is canned, and three other species besides the bluefin are sold under the name "tuna": the Albacore, *Thunnus germo*, the Yellowfin Tuna, *Neothunnus macropterus*, and the Skipjack, *Katsuwonus pelamis*. Well over two hundred million pounds are taken each year, of which two-thirds are composed of yellowfin tuna.

The largest bluefin tuna ever landed with fishing tackle was taken off Nova Scotia. It was nine feet, eight inches long and weighed 977 pounds. Specimens weighing 1,800 pounds have been reported, but such records have not been verified.

There is still a great deal that is unknown about the life history of the tunas. The bluefin is known to spawn in the western Mediterranean and just outside Gibraltar. There is evidence that the yellowfin reproduces during the summer off the west coast of Central America and near the Philippine, Caroline, and Marshall Islands and that the skipjack spawns around the Philippines. Without doubt other areas will come to light with further study. The eggs of the bluefin tuna are small and float for about two days, when they hatch. Growth is rapid, maturity being attained in three years, at a weight of about thirty pounds.

The Broadbill Swordfish, *Xiphias gladius,* roams the tropical and temperate seas of the world, hunting the fish and squid upon which it feeds. It has no teeth, but uses its sword—a tremendous extension of its upper jaw, composed of a flat, narrow, bony prolongation of the skull—to secure its prey.

The sword makes up about one-third of the giant fish's total length. It is used like the broadsword it resembles, being slashed to the right and left, through a school of herring and mackerel, killing or maiming numbers of fish that the swordfish can then consume with ease. More rarely the swordfish has been reported to impale prey on its sharp-pointed weapon. Undoubtedly fish are also sometimes caught without the aid of the sword, the swordfish depending upon its speed and size alone in these instances.

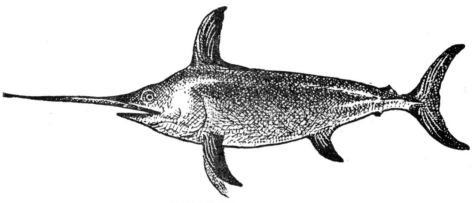

SWORDSMAN OF THE SEA

The broadbill swordfish may grow to a weight of six hundred pounds; much of this is highly palatable flesh, and the creature is much prized as a gamefish. Its famed sword is actually the upper jaw, drawn out to form a long, rigid beak. The broadbill uses this beak to cut left and right in a school of fish, and then consumes the victims.

The sword is also used in fighting. Broken-off pieces have been found embedded in sharks and in swordfish themselves. A considerable number of boats have been rammed by swordfish, the sword penetrating well over a foot into the hardwood of the vessel's side or bottom. Many harpooned or hooked swordfish have charged into small fishing craft and have driven their swords clean through and wounded the fishermen inside. In at least one instance a man was killed when he was pierced by a swordfish's sword that came up through the bottom of the dory in which he was lying.

Such incidents have given the swordfish the reputation of pugnacity, but the truth of the matter seems that the so-called attacks are more often the distracted rushes of a tormented fish rather than the deliberate charges of a vicious one.

Swordfish steaks are a delicacy; about four and one-half million pounds are fished or imported by Americans each year. Since ancient times, fishermen have captured swordfish—with harpoons, because of their large size. They are said to reach well over one thousand pounds, and four-hundred-pound specimens are not rare. Sport fishermen catch them "the hard way" on hook-and-line; the largest that was ever landed in this fashion weighed 860 pounds and was thirteen feet nine inches long.

The eggs of the swordfish are tiny, floating spheres about one sixteenth of an inch in diameter. The only definitely known spawning area is off northern Sicily, but there are undoubtedly several more undiscovered. Evidence that reproduction may also take place in the Black Sea and off the northern coast of Cuba has been accumulating. Baby swordfish are spiny-headed creatures, quite unlike their stream-lined parents. Both upper and lower jaws are long and provided with teeth. The teeth disappear relatively early in development, and the lower jaw gradually becomes shorter and shorter until it is less than one-third as long as the upper one which includes the long sword. Young swordfish are scaled, but by the time they are about four and one-half feet long all scales have been lost.

The broadbill swordfish is the sole member of the family Xiphiidae, a name derived from the Greek word for "sword".

The Atlantic Sailfish, *Istiophorus americanus,* looks like nothing so much as a torpedo when it flashes through the water, all its fins held close to its body, its enormous dorsal fin—from which it gets its name —being folded down into a deep groove along the back. Its dark blue back and light-coloured belly add to this illusion, and its sharp, cylindrical spear could well be taken as some strange sort of detonator for the sleek war head attached to it. The fish seems the very peak of streamlined form.

Like their relatives the marlins, the sailfishes are popular with big-game fishermen. There are several species, but apparently only one is found in the Atlantic. The Pacific Sailfish, *Istiophorus greyi,* is sometimes taken along the extreme southern coast of California. The Atlantic form is reported to reach 120 pounds, the Pacific species at least 190. Their average weights are about thirty-five and one hundred pounds, respectively. They are said to attain the phenomenal speed of sixty miles per hour under water, but this is for short distances only. The record Atlantic sailfish caught with rod-and-reel weighed 123 pounds and was ten feet four inches long.

Available evidence indicates that the Atlantic sailfish spawns during the summer. The very young fish have spiny heads and toothed jaws. During development both upper and lower jaws first become elongated, but only the upper one remains so, forming the spear. All spines and teeth are lost as the fish grows larger. The enlarged dorsal fin appears early in development, eventually becoming the enormous sail-like structure that is found in the adult.

The Blue Marlin, *Makaira nigricans ampla*, resembles the swordfish, but can readily be distinguished by its rounded spear, by its dorsal fin which extends much farther along the back and which can be depressed, fitting into a groove in the skin, and by the presence of

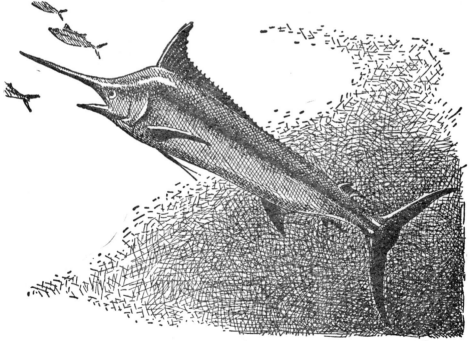

PRIZE CATCH FOR ANY FISHERMAN

The blue marlin provides a superb catch for even the most skilful of fishermen—this giant of the deep is sometimes more than twelve feet long, and puts up a strenuous fight for its life. On its upper jaw it carries a natural "marlinspike" which wins it its food; the fish owes its name to this weapon.

pelvic fins and peculiar thorn-like scales—both of which are absent in the swordfish. The shining, dark-blue back and silvery belly of the blue marlin make it one of the most beautiful of all of the big-game fishes. Its powerful, yet streamlined, body is a delight to the artist as well as to the sportsman.

The blue marlin occurs in the Atlantic Ocean and is found from Florida and the West Indies to Montauk Point, on the tip of Long Island, New York. There is another Atlantic species, the White Marlin, *Makaira albida*, that is much smaller, its maximum size being about half that of the average size of the blue marlin. The blue marlin averages about two hundred pounds. One twelve-hundred-pound giant has been recorded as caught in a net by Cuban fishermen. The record rod-and-reel catch weighed 742 pounds and was twelve feet ten and one-half inches long. In the Pacific, there are probably three species of marlin, the Striped Marlin, *Makaira mitsukuri*, being the one seen off southern California. The Black Marlin, *Makaira nigricans marlina*, found from Peru to New Zealand, may reach a length of fifteen feet and a weight of 1,226 pounds. It is the largest member of the group.

All of the marlins are much-sought-after game fishes. The thrill of having one of these fighting, swift-running, plunging, tail-dancing fish on the end of a line is perhaps the greatest in all fishing for sport.

We know very little about the life history of any of the marlins. They all feed on fish and squid. Sometimes they occur in numbers, but more often they are solitary. They are at times found in pairs, presumably for breeding. About all that is known regarding the spawning of the blue marlin is that most probably there are breeding grounds off Cuba and that reproduction occurs during the summer and early autumn. The marlin family (Istiophoridae or "sail-bearers") contains about ten different fishes, among them the spearfish and the sailfishes. All dwell in tropical and warm-temperate seas.

The Butter Fish, *Poronotus triacanthus*, lays its buoyant eggs during late June and July and August. Young specimens are often found under large jellyfish, where they apparently remain for protection. They also feed on small, swimming crustaceans close to shore—so close that they are sometimes thrown up on the beach by an unexpected wave.

Larger butter fish feed on small fishes, squid, and other creatures. They are a trim, silvery-blue fish, with a flat, deep, yet streamlined body and a strongly forked tail. They have no ventral fins, and this fact immediately distinguishes the species from the pompanos, which, at first glance, they resemble. Butter fish reach a length of a foot and a weight of one and one-quarter pounds. They are found along the Atlantic coast of North America from Nova Scotia to Florida. For years this delicious table fish was discarded, or used for fertilizer or cat food. Now about twelve and one-quarter million pounds are caught annually for man's consumption.

Butter fish belong to the family Stromateidae, which is sometimes placed in the order Scombroidei, sometimes put by itself. Its members possess sacs, lined with teeth, on either side of the gullet, and have peculiar ventral fins which, when present, have a membrane connecting the inner margin with the abdomen. The California Pompano, *Palometa simillima*, is not a true pompano, but is just as highly prized for food. It is similar in appearance to the butter fish, to whose family it belongs, but is slightly smaller, attaining a length of ten to eleven inches. It ranges along the coast from southern California to British Columbia.

Also included in the group is the Man-of-War Fish, *Nomeus gronovi*. This small species is found in tropical seas, often among the stinging tentacles of various jellyfishes, including the notorious Portuguese man-of-war. In times of danger, it dodges among these death-dealing filaments with apparent immunity, although merely to touch them spells death to other small fishes.

Gobies—Bottom-Dwellers

EVEN THOUGH the gobies are found over most of the world, you cannot blame yourself if you have overlooked them till now. They are small creatures and timid ones, and they love to hide on the bottom. That bottom may be of almost any kind—of a swift-flowing stream or a swamp, a mudflat or a tide pool, or near a sandy beach or a coral reef.

Some of the great legion of gobies (we know about seven hundred

different species, order Gobioidei, or "goby-like") can make themselves at home in both salt and fresh water. Some, when the pond or
stream dries up, can sleep away the summer in mud. Several make a
truly peculiar choice of living quarters, taking up residence in the
cavities of living sponges. There are blind gobies, too—but they
hardly need to see, for they live in places of perpetual darkness: underground rivers in Madagascar and West Australia, rocky crevices and
shrimp burrows on the California coast, and muddy waters in the
Indo-Pacific.

Still, all of those interesting creatures might seem commonplace
compared to one goby of the West Indies. This little fellow has the
curious habit of entering the mouths of large groupers grunts, parrot
fishes, and others. What does it do there? It picks at their teeth and
gums, much the way the Egyptian plover picks the teeth of crocodiles.
Like other gobies, it is very fond of flesh.

Far and away the largest family of gobies—it outnumbers the others
in species and individuals—is the Gobiidae. We know more about
the way these gobies reproduce than we do for the rest. Their eggs
come in a great variety of shapes: from spherical, through pear-shaped
and teardrop-shaped, to those that roughly resemble a marlinspike or
belaying pin in outline. Fastened to some underwater object, the
eggs are frequently guarded by the male. In some species, the larvae,
after being hatched in fresh water, float downstream to the sea, but
return to fresh water while still quite young. The California blind
goby and the pygmy gobies—more about them in a moment—are
members of this family.

Most gobies never reach six inches in length. But a few grow to be
twenty inches long, and two feet is probably the top size for any of
the order. The largest of the gobies are the sleepers (family Eleotridae).
Many of these live in fresh water; some, we believe, travel downstream
to spawn in the sea.

Along the tropical shores of Africa, Asia, and Australia, we come
upon the mudskippers and their relatives (family Periophthalmidae),
creatures strange in both appearance and habits. As the tide recedes
and lays great mudflats bare, the mudskippers can often be seen right
out in the open, hopping about on their powerful pectoral fins, which
they use like limbs, their protruding eyes turning from side to side to
seek their prey.

We have seen that most of the gobies are bottom-dwellers. When

A FISH THAT ACTS LIKE A FROG

In behaviour, as well as appearance, the mudskipper resembles a frog, but it is a true fish. In order to demonstrate its ability to travel on land, a corrugated paper ramp was built. The mudskipper, as these striking photographs reveal, showed no hesitation in using it.

The mudskipper's head is particularly froglike with its bulging eyes, its broad, round face, and its wide mouth.

The mudskipper can use its two ventral fins, which are united at the base, as a sort of pedestal (*bottom picture*). See page 1601.

Lilo Hess—Three Lions

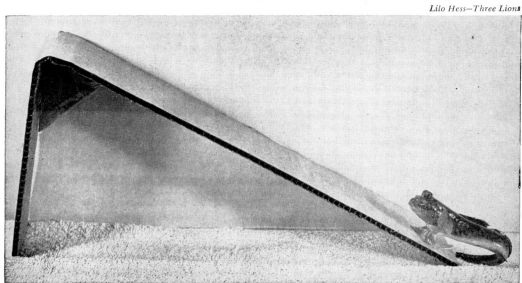

Lilo Hess—Three Lions

By rowing movements of its pectoral fins, the mudskipper inched itself up the ramp, resting on its ventral fins in between these strenuous efforts.

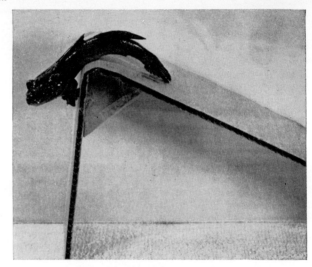

Over the top! The fish showed no hesitation at all in taking the short dive. In nature it takes much greater ones.

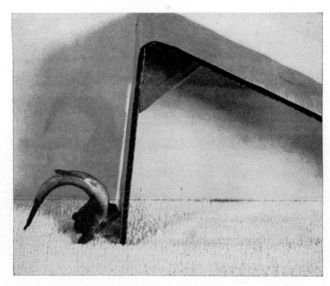

Not much grace, but effective none the less. Mudskippers are agile, and quick enough to catch insects on the wing.

we examine them closely we can readily observe how well suited they are for such an existence. Except for the family of sleepers, they often have a sucking disc by means of which they can fasten themselves to rocks or other objects on the bottom. This disc is formed by the pelvic fins—they are united at the base. A goby has its pelvic fins under or just in front of the pectorals, and there are spines in its fins, but they are weak as a general rule. There are about six families all told. The gobies are commonest in the tropics and inhabit at least some fresh waters on every continent and all but the coldest of shallow ocean waters.

The California Blind Goby, *Typhlogobius californiensis,* spends most of its life inside the burrow of a certain species of shrimp. From the age of six months or less until death—a period of perhaps ten years —it lives with a pair of these shrimps.

The blind goby shares not only their home but their fate as well. The dwelling consists of several small, connecting tunnels, with three or four very small openings. The tunnels are dug in the gravel between high and low water along the shores of southern California. The fish is completely dependent upon the shrimps for its shelter, since it is unable to dig or repair a burrow for itself. If both shrimps die the fish soon perishes also.

The host of the blind goby belongs to the group of ghost shrimps. It is a whitish-yellow creature, less than three inches long, shaped not unlike an ordinary crayfish. It feeds on tiny particles of organic matter that it sifts out of the water it constantly pumps through its burrow. This current also provides the blind goby with food, for the fish consumes any pieces of seaweed or animals that might be carried into the burrow and are too large for the shrimp. Although the goby thus helps keep the burrow clean, it has been shown that in captivity at least, a pair of shrimps can do very well without such guests.

The blind goby, too, usually lives in pairs, one pair to each burrow. The fish is small and pink; its colour results from the blood that shows through the colourless, translucent skin. The eyes are hardly visible, being degenerate and covered with several layers of skin, but although the fish cannot see, it is somewhat sensitive to strong light. The senses of touch and smell seem fairly well developed. The pelvic fins are arranged to form a sucking pad by which the blind goby can cling to smooth objects.

EAL / 13—E

The old saying about two being company and three a crowd, definitely holds for blind gobies. Should a second male put in an appearance, the original one will immediately engage it in fierce combat. The fight may last for hours, the fish biting each other and holding on with bulldog-like tenacity. The battle usually continues until one of the adversaries is killed or, less frequently, is driven from the burrow. If an extra female enters, it is the two females that battle to the death. If the interloper should win, he or she is accepted by the mate of the defeated fish without hesitation. Sex recognition has been shown to occur through chemical means.

The blind goby breeds from May until July. The ellipsoidal eggs are about one thirty-second of an inch long when first laid, but they subsequently grow to almost four times their length. From twenty-five hundred to fifteen thousand of them are deposited on the sides of the burrow. Both male and female fan the eggs and watch over them, either taking turns or working together. After ten to twelve days the eggs hatch. The young blind gobies are coloured, and have well-developed eyes. They are attracted to light, and this may be the reason that they soon leave the shrimps' burrow. By the time they are six months old, they have lost their dark coloration and their eyes have become distorted and partially overgrown with flesh.

The Dwarf Pygmy Goby, *Pandaka pygmaea*, is the smallest of fresh-water fishes and the shortest backboned animal known. Adult females attain a length of seven-sixteenths of an inch and adult males never quite reach three-eighths of an inch. These tiny fish inhabit certain lakes on the island of Luzon in the Philippines. With the exception of their prominent black eyes, they are colourless and practically transparent.

The minute eggs of the dwarf pygmy goby are about one sixty-fourth of an inch in diameter—that is, smaller than the full-stop at the end of this sentence. They are quite large in relation to the size of the fish, however, and each female contains only twenty to forty of them. They are tied together by means of numerous intertwined filaments; when laid, they float and become entangled with algae and other small objects at the water's surface.

Another goby from the same island, the Sinarapan, *Mistichthys luzonensis*, is almost as small as *Pandaka*, exceeding it on the average by about one-eighth of an inch. Perhaps the most remarkable thing about this fish is that it exists in such numbers in Lake Buhi that, despite its diminutive size, it is used for food. Vast numbers are scooped or dipped up from the water to be sold in the market and eventually stewed with vegetables or made into fish cakes and fried in oil. It takes about sixteen thousand sinarapan to make up one pound. Like the dwarf pygmy goby, this fish reproduces by means of minute eggs.

Small as these gobies are, there are two fishes still smaller—if one uses weight instead of length as a standard. Both are tiny, slender, transparent fish from the Pacific Ocean. They have no common name, but belong to the genus *Schindleria*. The smaller, *Schindleria praematurus*, reaches a maximum length of slightly more than three-quarters of an inch, but most mature males do not exceed five-eighths of an inch and females with eggs eleven-sixteenths of an inch. Definitely lighter than the Philippine pygmy goby, this species weighs perhaps one quarter of an ounce, and is the lightest of all backboned animals.

Schindleria lives near or at the surface of the sea, amidst many larval fishes, which it resembles in general appearance. Regardless of immature characteristics, many individuals are fully adult, as evidenced by the presence of mature sex glands. Specimens are generally found not far from land, so we believe that the fish is not an inhabitant of mid-ocean but lives in the waters surrounding the islands of the southwest Pacific and eastern Australia.

The relationship of the genus *Schindleria* to other fishes is still a mystery; some scientists have thought it related to the halfbeaks, others have placed it among the blennies, but neither arrangement seems satisfactory. Until more specimens of these rare fishes, in various stages of development, can be obtained, their exact place in the animal kingdom will remain a matter for conjecture.

The Mudskipper, *Periophthalmus koelreuteri*, combines the attributes of both fish and frog. Although it is a true fish, it behaves in a most froglike manner, regularly coming out of the water and hopping about on mudflats and mangrove swamps.

Even the mudskipper's bulbous head is rather froglike: it has puffed out "jowls", a hemispherical snout, and eyes set in sockets that project clearly above the top of the head. The eyes are quite mobile, and besides turning about, they can "wink" in a most grotesque manner.

The mudskipper's pectoral fins are mounted on movable, fleshy bases, and the fish "rows" itself along by means of them, dragging its elongated body behind. The pelvic fins also aid in this process, since they are located almost under the head and are united at the base and thus can act as a small pedestal to keep the head end of the fish off the ground. Mudskippers can leap as much as a yard, springing off the ground, mostly by means of the muscular tail, but also by using their pectoral fins. They sometimes leap from one mangrove root to another, and are said to be so agile that they can catch insects on the wing.

FISH OR FROG?

To the casual observer, the mudskippers seem to be half-frog, half-fish. What is more, these tropical oddities frequently leave the water and skip about vigorously on wet sand and mud in pursuit of insects. They must, however, make regular trips back to the water to moisten their skin and gills.

Mudskippers can remain out of water for a long time, but must periodically return to moisten their two bulging gill-chambers. By carrying a little of its native element with it, the mudskipper avoids being tied down to an aquatic life, although it never strays very far from water. It is widely distributed in shallow salt and brackish waters in the tropics, from the west coast of Africa, the Red Sea, the Indian Ocean and the western Pacific as far east as Polynesia. Experts have not yet decided how many different species of mudskippers occupy this vast area, or whether they all belong to a single species.

Mudskippers feed on insects and small crabs and reach a maximum length of nine inches. They apparently have a well-developed sense of proprietorship and often chase one another. At such times they flash their dorsal fins up and down, apparently using them as a signal device, or for bluffing. They also make burrows in the mud, in which the eggs are supposed to be laid and carefully guarded.

Fishes with Armoured Cheeks

IN THE strange underwater menagerie of this group you will find a zebra fish—a sea robin and a sea raven—scorpion fishes—rockfishes and stonefishes—and even a miller's thumb! So beautiful or fantastic are some of these creatures that every other domain of nature had to be ransacked to find names for them.

But so deadly, too, are a number of these fishes that they must be approached or handled with the greatest of care, even by experts. Some bear sharp spines equipped with poison glands and rank among the most poisonous fishes we know. They are capable of inflicting wounds causing intense suffering and even death.

These fishes, by and large, have one strong, distinguishing feature—their cheeks are armoured. A bony plate or rod runs from under the eye back into the gill cover. Some lack this plate, but the typical fish of the group has a bony ridge that is quite apparent, and it is spiny and rough on the outside. Sometimes we find the head completely covered with spiny bones. These natural warriors of the seas have pointed teeth that add to their savage appearance, and often they are eaters of flesh.

If we were to look for living masterpieces of camouflage, we would find an abundance of them among the scorpion fishes and their relatives (family Scorpaenidae). These rugged fishes carry numerous spines and tabs of flesh that allow them to blend in with the weeds among which they swim. Their colour, too, makes it hard to tell them apart from underwater rocks. Some, however, vie in hue with the most gorgeous of fishes. Perhaps their bright colours serve as a warning, because their spines are frequently dangerous, the slightest prick producing agonizing pain.

The scorpion fishes are at home in all the oceans, and like shallow water as well as deep; only a few prefer streams and rivers. Generally they do not grow over a foot in length, but there are some three-foot giants. We know about 250 species, among them the rockfishes and the rosefish—we shall return to them a bit later—being important as foodfishes. Some reproduce by means of floating eggs, others bring forth their young alive.

Also equipped with extremely poisonous spines—deadly, in some instances—are the stingfishes, or stonefishes (family Synanceidae). These fishes look like the scorpions, and rarely exceed a length of one foot. They are especially adept at concealing themselves on the bottom of the tropical tide pools that they frequent. We suppose that they lay eggs, but we know little about their life history.

The sea robins and the gurnards (the latter name comes from an old word meaning "grunt", and that is just what these fishes often do) grow over two feet long and are used for food in Europe and South Africa. The common American sea robins, on the other hand, are rarely eaten. Fishes of this family (Triglidae) hatch from pelagic eggs —eggs that float on the open sea—but spend most of their life in shallow water, on the bottom of tropical and temperate seas. They give the appearance of walking across the ocean floor on the several "fingers" that make up the pectoral fin.

Anglers of the west coast of the United States—especially in the area of Puget Sound—need no introduction to the greenlings (family Hexagrammidae). Both the greenlings and the skilfishes (family Anoplopomidae) dwell in the North Pacific. Their flesh is palatable, but only the Sable Fish, *Anoplopoma fimbria*, a dark grey or green creature, is commercially fished to any extent. It reaches three feet in length and forty pounds in weight. Still, it seems puny beside the Giant Skilfish, *Erilepis zonifer*—specimens of this fish six feet long and weighing more than two hundred pounds have been caught.

It is mainly in the waters of the Indo-Pacific that we encounter a group of fishes with a humble name but great value in the larders of mankind. These are the flatheads (family Platycephalidae). Each year the fish markets of Australia sell millions of pounds of flatheads. As both scientific and popular names suggest, these creatures have broad, flattened heads. The bottom of the ocean is where they live, and they inhabit shallow as well as deeper waters. Most flatheads are under three feet long, and there are about fifty species.

The short, sharp spines of the sculpins probably serve to hold off their enemies. These fishes favour cool or cold temperatures, and the three hundred species we know of inhabit salt and fresh water, shallow and deep. Often the angler pulls them from the streams and rivers of Europe, North America and Asia, and is disappointed at the small size of his catch. Freshwater sculpins—they are better known as bullheads, mudlers, or miller's thumbs—seldom reach six inches in length. Their cousins in the waters of the North Atlantic and Pacific and the Arctic oceans, however, may grow to over two feet long. A number of species have broken with one of the commonest of fish habits— they fertilize the eggs *before* they are laid. Often the male stays quite close to them and drives off any fish that dares to come near. (The sculpins make up the family Cottidae.)

We see the same protective habit among those plump, ungainly creatures known as the lumpfishes or lumpsuckers (family Cyclopteridae). They are strictly ocean fishes, and they patrol much the same chill waters the sculpins do. As you might suspect from their name, the lumpsuckers possess a sucking disc that they use to fasten themselves to rocks. Some lumpsuckers reach a length of about two feet.

Earlier, we talked of the armour that covers the heads of fishes of this order, either partly or completely. (The order name, Cataphracti, means "wholly enclosed".) What other major features do they have in common? In a group that includes about twenty families we may expect great variety. Still, we do find that the fins, dorsal and anal especially, are usually well equipped with spines, although these are lacking in some species or are so modified towards the ordinary soft fin ray that we can scarcely recognize them as spines. The ventral fins are present in most species, and are located forward, close to the pectorals.

The Rosefish, *Sebastes marinus,* was once a neglected marine food resource. Until 1935 it was marketed only in limited quantities, but then new methods of filleting, scaling and quick-freezing made it more saleable. By 1946, about 178 million pounds were caught in a single year for food. Since that time, however, the catch has fallen off somewhat. The fish is frequently sold as "ocean perch".

The rosefish is a bright red, varying to brownish or greyish red. It is more or less perchlike in general shape, but can be quickly distinguished from the perches by its pointed gill covers on which are located a number of spines. The single dorsal and anal fins are also strongly spined. A maximum size of three feet has been attained. Those along the Atlantic coast of North America rarely exceed two feet, however. At this length they weigh about thirteen pounds. They are fished at depths of three hundred to seven hundred and fifty feet, almost entirely by otter trawl.

Rosefish are cold water inhabitants, never being found in less than ninety feet of water during the summer even as far north as the Gulf of Maine. They are well known in the Arctic Ocean. They occur as far south as New Jersey in the western north Atlantic, and as far south as the English Channel in the east.

Although the rosefish gives birth to living young, these are born in a relatively undeveloped state. They show, in fact, very little advancement over typical fishes that have just been hatched from the egg. Examination has revealed that the young are not nourished by their mother—as in the great majority of live-bearing fishes—but simply rest within her, still inside their individual eggs. They hatch out inside the mother very shortly before being expelled. About all a mother rosefish does for her brood is to protect it until hatching.

Unlike the broods of other live-bearing fishes, the size of this one's is enormous. At birth each baby is about a quarter of an inch long, and a good-sized female may carry several thousand at one time. A thirteen-inch specimen contained approximately 20,500 young ready to be born. For some time after birth young rosefish float in the sea, pretty much at the mercy of their surroundings.

Rosefish are born from April, up to and including August, the time varying with the locality. Growth is extremely slow; it takes ten years to reach a size of eight inches. The rosefish feeds on various crustaceans, molluscs, and other invertebrates, and on small fishes, including young of its own species.

The Orange Rockfish, *Sebastodes pinniger,* is one of over fifty species of rockfishes that inhabit the shallow and deeper waters along the North American Pacific coast from California to Alaska. They are important foodfishes, more than thirteen million pounds having been taken in a single year in California. The orange rockfish is at present the most important single species of rockfish in the commercial catch of that state. The fish are taken with trawls and hook-and-line. Lines as long as one mile, carrying three thousand baited hooks, have been used.

The orange coloration of the body and fins of this fish distinguishes it from almost all other rockfishes. It has three bright orange stripes running across its spiny head, and the lining of its large mouth is pale red with dark mottling. It reaches a length of two and one-half feet.

The range of the orange rockfish extends from northern Baja California to northern British Columbia. It produces living young, apparently in the spring. The young are less than half an inch long at birth and still carry a yolk sac. They must float helplessly in the water for quite a while after birth. Large females may carry as many as six hundred thousand young. The younger fish inhabit waters near shore; old individuals have been found in water one hundred fathoms deep.

The Zebra Fish, *Pterois volitans,* as it floats majestically through the water, its queer fins gracefully waving and undulating, looks more like an apparition than a fish. It has its very large dorsal and pectoral fins separated, each fin-ray or spine being free of the others and having its own narrow strip of fin. This, together with its large, spotted pelvic, anal, and caudal fins, the bold black and white striping on its body, and the peculiar fleshy decorations around its eyes and mouth, makes the zebra fish at once one of the most bizarre and beautiful of all the sea's inhabitants.

That this fish is a menace is quickly apparent to anyone touching its spines, however, for they are quite poisonous and can cause much pain. Its gluttonous appetite is also quite matter of fact. In nature the zebra fish preys upon other living fishes, but in captivity it can be taught to eat pieces of dead fish and clam. Care must be taken not to overfeed captive specimens, because zebra fish have been known actually to gorge themselves so much that they died of indigestion or something akin to it.

Zebra fish sometimes seem to exert a weird immobilizing effect on the small fish upon which they prey. Instead of fleeing as it ordinarily would at the approach of a large fish, the prospective prey remains as if transfixed, quivering violently, until with a sudden gulp the zebra fish swallows it. This member of the family of scorpion fishes is widely distributed in the Indian Ocean and South-west Pacific. It reaches a length of somewhat over one foot.

The Stonefish, *Synanceja verrucosa*, and its close relatives are undoubtedly the most poisonous of all fishes. Along the stonefish's back is a series of thirteen large spines. Each of these has a pair of small sacs of venom attached to it, so arranged that any pressure exerted on the spine will cause the sacs to eject their poisonous fluid along the shallow grooves on either side, and to enter any wound made by the sharp-pointed spine. The venom is a limpid, bluish, slightly acrid fluid that causes excruciating pain. Men who have received the full force of the stonefish's poison have rolled on the ground, become delirious, attacked people trying to help them and even tried to amputate the affected limb—so great was their agony. Death may result from severe shock, heart failure, or, later, infectious poisoning. The wounds heal very slowly; recovery is a matter of months.

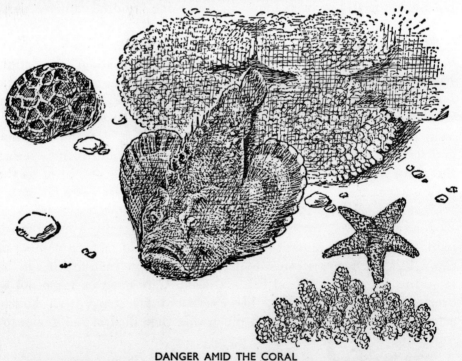

DANGER AMID THE CORAL

The stonefish is coloured like the rocks of coral among which it lives, but it is far deadlier than they. One of the scorpion fishes, this dangerous creature has on its back poison-bearing spines that can inflict a wound which is exceedingly painful, if not fatal. Fortunately the fish dwells only in some of the tropical seas.

The stonefish habitually lies on the bottom around tropical reefs and inlets. It has a flattened, short, triangular body with a large mouth whose gape is almost vertical. Its whole body is covered with warty growths, and in life it looks exactly like a piece of eroded coral. It feeds on a variety of creatures that it apparently engulfs with its cavernous maw as they unsuspectingly swim by its place of concealment.

Stonefish do not retreat even when approached by a large animal, apparently depending on their camouflage and poison for protection. Thus it is very possible for them to be stepped on unwittingly. Fortunately they seem to be nowhere common, although they are found over a large part of the Indian Ocean and the waters around northern Australia, the East Indies, and the Pacific islands. They attain a length of about one foot.

The Common Sea Robin, *Prionotus carolinus,* can be quickly recognized by the bony plates covering its head, by its two dorsal fins, and by its very large, winglike pectorals at the bottom of which are

FISH THAT "WALK" AND "SING"

The common sea robins, two of which are pictured above, are sometimes reported to have been seen walking on the sea bottom. They are without feet, but there are rays on the pectoral fins which look like feet—with these the fish examine the ocean floor. The creatures can produce a cackling sound by means of their swim-bladder

located three free, thickened rays. These are bent like arched fingers and seem to be walked on as the fish moves along the bottom. The chances are that any fish from the east coast of the United States, described by the uninitiated as having "feet", is one of the sea robins. These rays are undoubtedly used by the fish to explore the bottom. Common sea robins feed principally on small crustaceans that live on or near the bottom. Squid, bivalves, worms, and fishes are taken to a lesser extent.

This fish spawns during the summer. The female lays slightly yellowish, buoyant eggs, about one-thirty-second of an inch in diameter. They hatch in about sixty hours at 72 degrees Fahrenheit. The larvae are a little less than one-sixteenth of an inch long at hatching. The maximum length is about sixteen inches.

The common sea robin is found in shallow waters from the Bay of Fundy to South Carolina, but it is rare north of Cape Cod. During the cold months it disappears from New England and New Jersey, while remaining in Chesapeake Bay and more southern waters all the year round.

By means of special muscles that vibrate its swim-bladder, the common sea robin makes noises, described as a rhythmic squawk, squeal, or cackle, such as might be heard in a barnyard. These sounds are also said to be similar to those made by drawing one's forefinger and thumb towards each other over the dry surface of an inflated rubber balloon.

The Sea Raven, *Hemitripterus americanus,* looks extremely ragged because of the numerous fleshy tags on its head and the jagged profile of its dorsal fin—which has the individual spines separated from one another and tipped with tiny flaps as if the fish had just come through some terrible ordeal. The entire skin is prickly. Coloration ranges from blood red through reddish purple to chocolate and yellowish brown.

Sea ravens are bottom-inhabiting sculpins; they feed on various invertebrates and on other fishes, which they catch with their large sharp-toothed mouths. During the winter sea ravens come closer to shore than in the warmer months, since they quite definitely prefer cold water. They are found from Labrador, Newfoundland and the Grand Banks south to Chesapeake Bay.

Adhesive eggs, with a diameter of about five thirty-seconds of an inch and ranging in colour from bright orange to pale yellow, are laid among the fingers of sponges from mid-October to late December at the latitude of New York. Hatching probably does not take place until after several months. The larvae are not quite half an inch long when they first emerge from the egg. At the age of one and one-half years, young sea ravens are about six inches long. A maximum length of twenty-one and three-quarter inches and a weight of five pounds five ounces has been reported."

The Miller's Thumb, *Cottus bairdi,* is a small, grotesque fish from the streams and lakes of eastern North America. It prefers cool, clear water with a rocky or gravelly bottom. It often hides under stones, rarely swimming in mid-water. Its large head is bony and flattened, with the eyes located high on the sides. The body sharply tapers down towards the tail and is practically naked. The pectoral fins are large. A length of seven inches may be attained, although most adult specimens range between three and five inches.

During spring and early summer, masses of adhesive eggs are laid, usually attached to the underside of stones or, more rarely, on aquatic plants. The male prepares the nesting site and generally guards the eggs. Two or three females may lay in a single nest. The salmon-coloured eggs are large, being about one-eighth inch in diameter. Miller's thumbs principally eat algae, small fishes, and crustaceans, and aquatic insects and their larvae. They consume the eggs of other fishes, when they can get them, but have been cleared of the charge of destroying significant quantities of trout eggs.

The Lumpfish, *Cyclopterus lumpus,* is just that—a lump of a fish. It is short from head to tail and deep from back to belly. The belly is wide and flattened while the back is narrow and rigid, giving the fish a triangular cross section. The back is also strongly arched from head to tail, and the skin is covered with wartlike tubercles in place of scales. The ventral fins are modified into a sucker, located just behind the throat. The fish may be grey, brown, yellow-green, or slate-blue in colour. During the spawning season the lower portions of the male's body become bright red.

As many as 136,000 adhesive eggs are laid by a single female in large spongelike clumps during the late winter and spring. These are faithfully guarded and cared for by the male, who blows water through the egg mass, fans it with his pectoral fins and drives away all intruders, including fishes larger than himself. If the water temperature is low, hatching may take two months, at the end of which time the father fish appears quite worn out. The eggs are pink when first laid, but change colour as they develop. They are about one-eighth of an inch in diameter.

Newly hatched lumpfish are about a quarter of an inch long, and fully equipped with a tiny sucker which they use to fasten themselves to seaweed and other drifting objects.

Adult lumpfish inhabit cool waters off the coast of North America from Hudson Bay and Greenland south to New Jersey and, exceptionally, Maryland. To the east they are found along the coast of Europe south to the Bay of Biscay. Although lengths of two feet and weights of twenty pounds may be reached, most specimens are considerably smaller.

Flatfishes—They Swim on Their Side

No DOUBT you have met the halibut, the flounder, and the sole so many times at the dinner table that you consider them among the most commonplace of fishes. Yet people who see them alive—who watch the strange way they grow—feel that they are entitled to a place in the front rank of nature's wonders!

These ordinary-seeming creatures go by the name of flatfishes, and flat they are. But that is not what is really curious about them. The odd fact is that after having passed their babyhood swimming like other fishes, they make a remarkable change—they turn on their sides, and spend the rest of their lives swimming in that way.

Even more noteworthy than all this is what happens to the fish's eyes. Earlier in the normal position, they make the change, too: they move to the top side of the head. Now we call this the "eyed side"; the other, on which the fish lies, is the "blind side". The skull and jaws, gill-covers, paired fins, lateral line, and other organs alter as part of this extraordinary shift, so that they may best serve the flatfish in its new, one-sided way of life. (The flatfishes belong in the order Heterosomata, which means "different bodies".)

At the same time, the colour changes in most of the flatfishes. Just one side—the side bearing the eyes—has pigment in it. The "blind side" becomes plain white. You may expect exceptions here as elsewhere, and we find some abnormal fishes with colour on top and bottom, others with no colour at all.

When the flatfishes swim they keep their whole body in a plane, more or less parallel to the ocean floor. As a rule, they make their home on the bottom of the sea, most of them staying rather near shore. Sometimes a number may venture up rivers, and there are members of the sole and tonguefish families that live entirely in fresh water. By and large the six hundred or so different kinds of flatfishes lay eggs that float in mid-water or at the surface. The winter flounder, whose ways we shall soon examine more closely, is a notable exception.

One sure way of recognizing the flatfishes, we have seen, is by the eyes, which are always on one side of the head. But which side? That depends on the species. The turbot, European brill, summer flounder, and sundial (family Bothidae)—found widely scattered through temperate and tropical seas, mainly—have eyes on their left side. The opposite is true of the halibuts, winter flounder, plaice, lemon sole, yellow-tail, and starry flounder (family Pleuronectidae). However, driving home again the great truth that nature is variable and that it is a rare generalization that fits all the facts, a few species regularly show individuals with eyes on the left. The fishes of this family are salt-water-dwellers, and we encounter them practically all over the world, from the Arctic almost to the Antarctic.

North Americans are fond of fillet of sole, but many have learned by now that it comes from other fishes masquerading under that title for the chef's convenience. The true soles (family Soleidae), including the hogchoker, do dwell in North American waters, but those of economic importance are found around Europe and South Africa. It is in warm-temperate and tropical seas that they are most numerous, and the same are also the home of the tonguefishes (family Cynoglossidae). But though the tonguefishes and the soles may meet, they cannot see eye to eye: the first have their vision on the left side, the second on the right.

The Pacific Halibut, *Hippoglossus stenolepis,* has had the distinction of being studied by an International Fisheries Commission set up by Canada and the United States especially for that purpose. Alarmed by the decline of the fishery, these countries in 1924 ratified a treaty that created a body of scientific experts to find out the essential facts in the life history and fishing of the Pacific halibut. No idle business, this. Proper regulations were needed to place the fishery on a sound basis for the years to come, but first there had to be sound knowledge.

In 1930 the recommendations of this group of scientists were accepted by both governments and a new treaty was signed, giving the Commission power to regulate the fishery. Although the efficacy of its rule has been argued both pro and con, the fact remains that Pacific halibut fishing has improved in recent years.

Approximately fifty million pounds of Pacific halibut are now taken annually. The fish are caught by hook-and-line in waters ranging from ten to five hundred fathoms deep. The fish is marketed fresh or frozen and the liver and other viscera are treated to yield valuable, vitamin-rich oil. As an example of international co-operation for the purpose of advancing the cause of conservation, and the intelligent, long-term utilization of a natural resource, the case of the Pacific halibut is classic.

Pacific halibut reach a weight of at least 470 pounds and an age of thirty-five years or more. Like all the flatfish, they lie upon their sides as they rest upon the bottom.

The story of how the Pacific halibut grows and develops is more curious than any you can find in fiction. When first hatched out of its egg, a baby Pacific halibut is not unlike many other larval fishes—it has an eye on either side of its head, and it soon grows normally located fins. It stays this way from a size of about five-sixteenths of an inch (the size at hatching) until the baby is about nine-sixteenths of an inch, but at this time peculiar changes start to take place.

Little by little, the baby's left eye becomes elevated above the right one and shortly afterward the right eye begins to move down on its side of the skull. The left eye now makes an amazing migration from the left to the right side of the head of the fish. Meanwhile the pigment on the left side has not developed as much as that on the right. The body broadens—from back to belly—and by the time the fish is about one and a quarter inches long, the baby Pacific halibut looks very much like a miniature adult, with both eyes on the right side of its

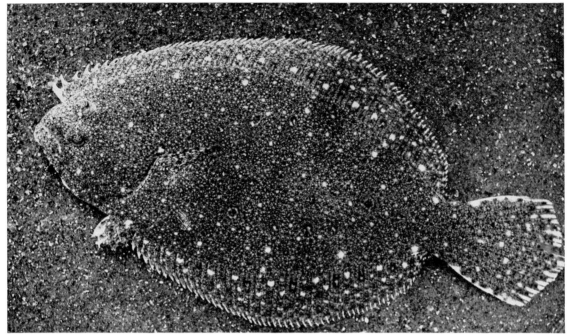

U. S. Fish and Wildlife Service Photos

CAMOUFLAGE ARTISTS

The gulf flounder, *Paralichthys albiguttus*, is closely related to the fluke and, like that fish, can change its colours to match the natural background upon which it is resting. It does this by expanding or contracting the pigment within the thousands of pigment cells in its skin. This species has its eyes and pigment on the left side, and lies on its right side, which is more or less colourless. It is able only to approximate an artificial background. See page 1612.

New York Zoological Society Photos

THE PORCUPINE FISH PUFFS ITSELF UP FOR PROTECTION

After blowing itself up with either air or water, the porcupine fish appears droll to us, but to a hungry fish it must seem a most unappealing morsel. Nevertheless, porcupine fish have been occasionally found in the stomachs of larger fishes. See *page 1629.*

head and with the left or "blind side" practically devoid of pigment. The right or "eyed side" is coloured a dark brown or grey. The fish thus lies on its left side on the bottom, and when it swims it keeps its eyed side uppermost, its blind side facing the bottom.

As a result of the investigations of the International Commission, we know a great deal about the Pacific halibut. There are still, however, many things about the fish we should know but do not. On the average, females mature when twelve years old, but males do so when considerably younger. Spawning occurs from November to January. A female weighing 140 pounds may produce as many as 2,700,000 eggs. These eggs are relatively large, being more than one-eighth of an inch in diameter. They float freely in deep water until hatching, after which the larvae, too, continue to live in mid-water. When four or five months have passed, they rise toward the surface to be carried inshore by winds and currents. Here the young change into small halibut, and take up their life on the bottom. During this long period the eggs and young are at the mercy of the elements and their predatory enemies: consequently the death rate is very heavy.

Unlike many flatfishes, halibut not only feed upon fishes, crabs, clams, and worms that live on the bottom, but actively pursue prey, such as squid and fast-moving fishes.

The Pacific halibut ranges from the Bering and Okhotsk Seas south to California. The fishing regions or banks run along the coast of North America from the south-western tip of Alaska to Washington.

The Atlantic Halibut, *Hippoglossus hippoglossus,* can be distinguished from the Pacific species by its somewhat differently shaped body and by its scales and the way they are set in the skin. Said to attain weights of seven hundred pounds, this is the largest of all the flatfishes. These giants may live as long as forty years. The Atlantic halibut is found in the North Atlantic as far south as New York and the Bay of Biscay.

The Summer Flounder or Northern Fluke, *Paralichthys dentatus,* possesses two distinct means of concealing itself as it rests on the bottom. One is by "bedding". As the fish comes to rest on a muddy or sandy bottom, it vibrates its body, fins, and tail in such a way that water currents are set up, carrying the loose material composing the bottom out from under it. The fish then quickly stops moving and drops to the bottom. The material stirred up settles on top of it, covering most of its body or, if the material is coarse, its edges.

The second method is "concealing coloration". The fish comes to match the background upon which it rests. It accomplishes this by changes in the various kinds of pigment cells that colour the eyed side. The summer flounder has remarkable powers of duplicating the visual effect of a muddy, sandy, gravelly, stony, or shell-covered bottom. On a very dark background the fish will become practically black, on a very light one, almost white. Blue, green, yellow, orange, pink, and various shades of brown are all excellently matched, but red is not. It takes several months, however, for the fish to assume a green or blue coloration, while yellows and brown can be duplicated in much less time. On the other hand, many changes in pattern, rather than hue, can be effected in a matter of minutes.

As startling as these colour and pattern changes are, the summer flounder cannot assume the appearance of a Scotch plaid, no matter how long it may be forced to live upon one!

All flatfishes apparently possess the power of matching their background to some degree; in the summer flounder it is especially well developed. Experiments have shown that the pigment cells are controlled by nerves, and that the fish must see its background to be able to match it. Blind summer flounders do not match their environment at all. It has also been demonstrated, however, that hormones influence the colour and pattern of the fish. Finally, we know that light, acting directly on the individual pigment cell, can also bring about pigmentation, because summer flounders that have their right, colourless and eyeless sides exposed to light—by being kept in a glass-bottom tank over electric lights—develop some pigment on that side, whether they are blind or not. Control of coloration in these fishes is therefore a complicated process.

As indicated above, the summer flounder rests on its right side, both of its eyes being on the left, in contrast to the halibut and winter flounder. Occasionally, a flatfish is *reversed*, that is, an individual belonging to a species normally having its eyes on its left side will have them on its right side instead and vice versa. At least one reversed summer flounder is on record; it had its eyes on the right side but was coloured on both sides.

Although there is little definite information on the reproductive habits of the summer flounder, all indications are that it spawns during the early winter and that the eggs are buoyant. It feeds on a variety of animal life, often rising to the surface in its efforts to catch fish. The maximum weight is twenty-six pounds but usually it does not exceed five. It is an excellent foodfish and a popular gamefish; well over eleven million pounds are caught yearly. It ranges along the Atlantic coast of the United States from Massachusetts to Florida.

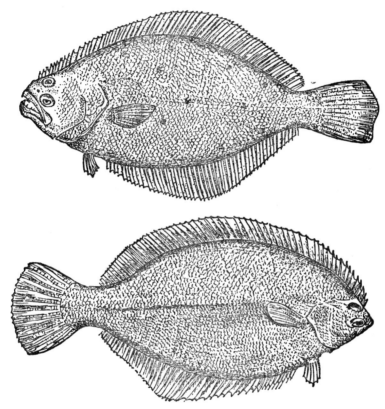

FLOUNDERS AND THEIR CURIOUS EYES

Flounders, or flatfishes have two eyes, all right—but both are on the same side; the fish lie on the other side, which is blind. The chief difference between the summer flounder (*top*) and the winter flounder (*bottom*) is that the eyes of the first are on the left, while the eyes of the second are on the right.

The Winter Flounder, *Pseudopleuronectes americanus,* lies on the bottom, and when some shrimp or crab appears, it rapidly pursues it, snaps it up, and again settles down to rest. Undoubtedly it also roots out some of its food, because bivalves and worms that live beneath the surface have been found in its stomach. Occasionally it catches small fish, but cannot eat large ones, as its mouth is rather small.

This species is a dextral or right-handed flatfish—that is, its eyes are both on the right side, and it lies on its colourless left side when resting. Sinistral, or left-handed, winter flounders, having eyes and pigment on the left side and no pigment on the right, are very rare.

A popular food and game fish, the winter flounder is well known to both commercial fishermen and those who fish for sport. It is found along the Atlantic coast of North America from Labrador to Georgia. In the warmer parts of its range the fish migrates offshore during the summer. A specimen of more than five pounds is very unusual; the record individual weighed slightly more than five pounds thirteen ounces, and was twenty-two inches long.

Reproduction takes place from mid-December to May in the vicinity of southern New England. In water from one to three fathoms deep, small groups of fish swim rapidly in tight circles, scattering the eggs and milt about in a manner reminiscent of the sparks from an old-fashioned pyrotechnic pinwheel. The tiny eggs stick together in clusters and sink to the bottom. They hatch in fifteen days at 69 degrees, the newly hatched fish being less than three-sixteenths of an inch long. Young winter flounders are occasionally found in fresh water in streams but never far from the sea. By the time they have become two to three years old, winter flounders have grown to between eight and ten inches in length.

The Starry Flounder, *Platichthys stellatus,* ranges along the West Coast of North America from southern California to Alaska, and in the Far East north from Japan and Korea. This species belongs to a family of flatfishes that are normally dextral; that is, they have their eyes and pigment on the right side. In many species in this family, an occasional abnormal sinistral individual turns up, but in the starry flounder a large percentage of these reversed fish, with colour and eyes on the left side, occurs. In California about half the starry flounders are reversed, in Alaska about two-thirds, and in Japan the great majority of individuals are sinistral.

The body of the starry flounder is covered with small, spinelike, star-shaped plates, from whence it gets its name. It grows to a size of twenty pounds but averages considerably less. The eggs are laid from early winter to early spring. A variety of invertebrates, including crabs, shrimps, worms, and bivalves, make up its food.

Adults usually live in shallow salt water, along the shore, sometimes venturing into deeper areas, but the young are often found in the fresh or brackish waters of the lower reaches of streams. Of the several species of flatfishes on the Pacific coast of North America, the starry flounder is the most important for sports fishing. It is also an important commercial foodfish.

The Common European Sole, *Solea solea,* provided the original fillet of sole, a great delicacy supposed by some epicures to be the most tasty of piscine dishes. Those foodfishes in North America called soles are not true soles. The true soles are characterized by their very flat, leaflike or tonguelike appearance, with dorsal, tail, and anal fins often continuous with one another, making a complete fringe around the body. The mouth, as well as the pair of eyes, is completely reoriented, being twisted almost completely on to the under-side of the head; that is, to the left side of the fish, while the eyes are located on the right side. The true soles found in North America, such as the hogchoker, are of practically no commercial value.

The common European sole is found from the North Sea to and throughout the Mediterranean. The usual size at which it is marketed is about eight inches. During the day soles hide most of the time, doing their feeding at night. They eat bottom-inhabiting forms like worms and shrimps, which they apparently detect by means of tiny filaments on the under-side of the head. Spawning occurs from April to August. The eggs float in mid-water, hatching in about ten days. Young soles frequent shallow water but move farther offshore as they grow larger.

Shark Suckers—Other Fishes Carry Them

THE SHARK SUCKER or remora has a "free ticket" to journey almost anywhere it wishes in the great watery world of our tropical and temperate seas. The vehicle it travels on may be a shark, a barracuda, a marlin, a swordfish, a whale, or even a ship. It carries its ticket with it always: a sucking disc on top of its head, enabling the remora to attach itself to these carriers and leave them at will.

For creatures that travel free of charge, the shark suckers are difficult to please when it comes to selecting their transportation. Of the ten or so species, some have a marked preference for one type of carrier, some for another. Usually, however, they show a certain amount of latitude in their choice.

Remoras attach themselves in some peculiar spots. Favourite places are inside the gill-cavities or mouths of large fishes like sharks, marine sunfishes, and the swordfish, for instance.

The largest of the remoras reach a length of three to four feet. All those alive today are placed in a single family (Echeneidae) in the order Discocephali—"disc-headed" is a literal translation.

The Shark Sucker, *Echeneis naucrates*, regularly takes free rides on large fishes and turtles, and sometimes on porpoises and ships, by fastening itself to them by means of a powerful sucker. This organ is located on the top of its head, and is a flat, oval plate with raised edges, having twenty or more narrow slats in its centre. These can be raised, thus creating a vacuum. They are also provided with tiny backward-pointing spines; when pressure is applied from the front, they prevent the shark sucker from sliding off the surface to which it is attached. Once a shark sucker has fastened itself, it cannot be removed by pulling on its tail, but must be slid off forwards or sideways, or the edge of the plate must be lifted to destroy the vacuum.

The shark sucker sometimes uses a shark only as a means of transportation, leaving its carrier in order to feed on small fishes. At other times it also shares the shark's food, picking up scraps from its table so to speak. Despite its "hitch-hiking" habits, the shark sucker can swim very well and rapidly on its own. It has to, in order to catch a ride on a swiftly moving fish.

This species is somewhat elongated with a rather long second dorsal and anal fin, and a squared-off tail fin. Its first dorsal fin is lacking, since it has become modified to form the sucker. The shark sucker has an undershot jaw, and it is provided with many small teeth.

Colour changes are very rapid; the fish may be almost black or almost entirely white, or marked with broad, longitudinal black and white stripes, changing pattern from one minute to the next. The shark sucker reaches a length of about two feet. It is found in all tropical seas, and during the warm months ventures into temperate zones. It has been reported as far north as Massachusetts on the east coast of North America and San Francisco on the west.

At one time in northern Australia, south-eastern Asia, western Africa, northern South America and the West Indies, the larger species of remoras were used for fishing. A line was attached to the fish's tail and it was allowed to swim about until it attached itself to some large fish or turtle. Then, by slow, steady pulling, both remora and the creature to which it was attached were brought to the fisherman's hands. As we have already suggested, the remora is unable to free itself if a pull directly backwards is exerted on it. This peculiar kind of fishing is still carried on with the shark sucker in some parts of the West Indies.

The feasibility of this method of fishing was once tested at the New York Aquarium. After placing a large shark sucker in a bucket filled with sea water, it was found that the whole bucket could be lifted off the ground by grasping the fish's tail. So strong was the suction developed that the two shark suckers tested supported buckets filled with water that weighed twenty-one and twenty-four pounds respectively.

So far as known, the remoras lay pelagic eggs. The larvae, up to a size of about one-third of an inch, have no sucker and float in the open sea.

Trigger Fishes, Trunkfishes, Puffers, and Their Relatives

IN THE TROPICS, in ocean waters of little depth, dwell the trigger fishes, the trunkfishes, the puffers, and their equally strange relatives. Often they throng the waters around coral reefs. They lack

a streamlined body, and, when danger approaches, you might expect
them to be somewhat at a loss.

Many of these fishes, however, are ready to meet all comers. They
have an array of spectacular defence mechanisms they can depend
upon. Some bristle with spines; some can turn a hard, bony shell to
bear the brunt of the onslaught; others can blow themselves up like a
balloon to foil the attacker. A number possess sharp teeth, capable
of inflicting painful wounds.

Large, rough scales cover the bodies of the trigger fishes (family
Balistidae), creatures that actually have a trigger mechanism in their
dorsal fin. We shall see later in this chapter how they use it. For most
of this large group, the central and western Pacific is home. Many
are extravagantly coloured, but the few that occur in warmer temperate
waters or offshore tend to be dull. The maximum size of practically
all lies between six inches and two feet. With their powerful teeth
they are able to cut into shells to get at the living animal inside.

Because their leathery skin is covered with tiny prickles making
it rough to the touch, another family is known as the filefishes
(Monacanthidae). They are shaped like their cousins the trigger fishes
but the body is narrower and the first dorsal fin is just a single long
spine. On the whole, they are small creatures—most are less than a
foot long. In tropical and warm-temperate seas they form a numerous
tribe.

Heavy armour is the hallmark of the trunkfishes (family Ostraciidae).
It does indeed form a kind of trunk to protect these creatures, but a
quite unusual one—it may have three, four, or five sides of hard bone.
There are about a score of these brightly coloured species dwelling in
tropical seas, the largest being twenty inches in length or longer. One
notable kind has hornlike spines projecting above the eyes; these
creatures are known as cowfishes.

The puffers, blowfishes, or swellfishes (family Tetraodontidae) are
aptly named. Most of them can blow themselves up with air or water
and assume a globelike shape. At such times, their mouths, eyes,
and fins seem dwarfed by comparison, so that the puffers appear to
be more a part of an underwater fantasy than creatures of flesh and
blood. In the bargain some are poisonous. The largest species attain
a length of three feet, but most are less than half this size. After laying
their heavy eggs in the warm waters they inhabit, the ocean puffers
give them no further care; in sharp contrast, the freshwater puffers

of the tropics guard their adhesive eggs and keep a parental eye on the newly hatched young.

Also at home in tropical and warm-temperate seas are the porcupine fishes and burr fishes or spiny box fishes (family Diodontidae). They resemble the puffers in size and can inflate themselves in the same way. But their numerous spines provide a clear means of telling them apart, and the beak is made up of two teeth instead of four as in the puffers. When they are puffed up, with their sharp prickles thrust out in every direction, the porcupine fishes look more like curious marine plants than fishes. There are some fifteen species.

To round off our picture of the strange forms of life that make up this group, we should take a glance at the headfishes (family Molidae). As they swim about in the water, they seem to be all head! Their deep bodies appear to be cut off behind the high dorsal and anal fins. But they actually do have a short fringe of a tail. Their skin is tough and leathery, and those who have tasted them say the same of the flesh. The ocean sunfish, reaching eleven feet, is the largest of the three species, the smallest being about three feet long. Sometimes they are seen sunning themselves in mid-ocean, but they may go down to great depths in their native tropical and temperate waters.

The members of this order are most closely related to the surgeon fishes, and there are seven to ten families in all. Because of certain peculiar features of the skull they are called Plectognathi ("joined jaws").

All species have small mouths, which they cannot extend. The outer openings of the gill cavities are small, and ventral fins are usually lacking; when present, they are little, and located near the pectorals. As we have seen, these fishes may be very unlike each other in appearance, some being covered with rough scales, others with prickly or leathery skin, or with a hard, bony shell.

The Common Trigger Fish, *Balistes carolinensis,* is known from both shores of the warmer parts of the Atlantic and also from the Indian Ocean. During the late summer and autumn it is a fairly regular visitor as far north as Massachusetts. Young specimens are common in floating seaweed and are undoubtedly carried north with these plants by the Gulf Stream.

A length of slightly more than two feet is attained by the common trigger fish. Like most members of its family, its body is compressed and somewhat rhomboid in profile, with the mouth, the trigger mechanism, the tail and ventral flap each located at one "corner". The anal and second dorsal fins extend along most of two of the "sides". In contrast to many other trigger fishes, which are armoured with enlarged bony scales, it has a leathery, yet rough, scaly skin. It is capable of colour changes, ranging from pale white to dusky brown, decorated with blotches or reticulations. The strong jaws and teeth are used to obtain both animal and vegetable food.

The fish's trigger mechanism is made up of the first three spines of the dorsal fin. The front one is quite stout and can be made to stand up by the fish, at will. The second spine fits into a groove at the back of the first, and when the two are erected, it slips snugly against the first and locks it in the erect position. Once locked, the strong first spine will break off before it can be depressed. The trigger is the still smaller third spine. This is connected to the second by a "ligament" so that depressing the third spine pulls the second away from the first and allows these two to move freely and fall backwards. The fish is able to move its third spine and thus can unlock its fin at will.

What practical purpose this arrangement serves we are not entirely sure. Perhaps the spines, when locked in an erect position, prevent the trigger fish from being eaten. They can also be employed, together with the ventral flap (that replaces the ordinary ventral or pelvic fins), to wedge the fish securely in crevices between rocks or coral formations, so that it cannot be removed. At the New York Aquarium trigger fishes frequently wedged themselves in the rockwork of their tanks, and many a visitor informed us that these fish were stuck there, not realizing that they could release themselves whenever they wanted.

The common trigger fish is frequently used for food, but many of the more brightly coloured species of trigger fishes of the tropical Pacific are reputed to have poisonous flesh. Some of these are members of the genus *Balistapus* that go by the musical Hawaiian name of *Humu-humu Nuku-nuku Apua-a*, which means "a spined fish with the snout or grunt of a pig".

The Orange Filefish, *Ceratacanthus schoepfi,* always looks as if it were half starved. Its flat, angular, bony body gives it the appearance of being chronically underfed. As it slowly pokes along, swimming by means of undulation of its dorsal and anal fins, with its little protruding mouth, small but prominent eyes, and single, coarse spine located just above them, it exhibits a gravely comic deportment.

Its skin is hard and rough, and was used as sandpaper at times in the past. It is variously mottled with orange, brown and black. The range of the orange filefish extends from Maine to Brazil. The fish feeds mostly on sedentary or fixed animals and plants which it nips off from their place of attachment by means of its sharp teeth. It attains a length of about two feet.

We know practically nothing about the spawning of the orange file-fish. Undoubtedly it lays buoyant eggs during the warmer months. Young specimens are frequently found along the east coast of North America during summer and early autumn. They frequently take up a position with their head pointed almost straight down. When in close association with underwater plants, young orange filefish at first glance seem to be plants themselves, both their colour and shape helping to create this illusion.

The Cowfish, *Acanthostracion quadricornis,* lives inside its own suit of armour which it carries around with it at all times. The scales on the fish's head and body have become modified into hexagonal plates, securely cemented together to form a hard, immovable case, covering the entire fish save where its fins, eyes, jaws, and tail project through. Just in front of the eyes a pair of small, sharp horns point forward and at the rear of the body there are three pairs of spines pointing backwards.

Like a tortoise the cowfish is encased in a rigid shell, and like a tortoise it cannot move very fast. Depending entirely on its dorsal and anal fins and, to a lesser extent, on its caudal and pectorals, the cowfish must "scull" or "row" itself through the water. Since it feeds upon worms and other small creatures ensconced in coral reef formations, by breaking down the sheltering stone with its powerful, sharp teeth, it need not swim fast in pursuit of prey.

Although they have lost the mobility of their bodies, cowfish have not lost the ability to alter their colours. Sometimes they are pure white, other times tan or brown with networks of light blue markings. Probably because their shell retains water around the gills, these fish can survive for two hours or more out of water.

The cowfish lays buoyant eggs about one thirty-second of an inch in diameter. In about two days they hatch into larvae that within a week have begun to develop the hard covering so characteristic of their parents. Adults reach a length of about one foot. They range on both sides of the tropical Atlantic, being fairly common as far north as the Carolinas. Cowfish may not look appetizing, but their flesh is delicious and is often cooked in the fish's own shell.

FISH THAT RESEMBLE COWS
The cowfish gets its name from two curious hornlike projections **above its eyes.** This fanciful-seeming creature is encased in a rigid sheath; it is not able to manoeuvre very well and is incapable of speed. Worms are among the cowfish's favourite foods, and it bites them out of coral reefs in the tropical Atlantic, its home.

The Northern Puffer, *Sphoeroides maculatus,* blows itself up with either air or water until its whole body is spherical, like a balloon, with only its fins and tail projecting. The water or air is pumped directly into the stomach, part of which is modified into a special, inflatable sac. The mouth cavity acts as the pump, its floor being capable of considerable expansion and contraction. Strong muscles at each end of the stomach prevent the escape of the fluid or gas from that organ until the puffer wishes to release it. An eight-inch specimen engulfs a little more than a quart of water in becoming fully inflated.

When blown up with water, the puffer is a difficult or impossible morsel for hungry predators to handle, and inflation with air can make it impossible for fish-eating birds to hold a puffer in their claws.

Puffers themselves are savage predators, however, and are provided with four very strong, sharp, nipping teeth. They feed on crabs, bivalves, snails, barnacles, and a variety of other invertebrates. When tackling a large crab, puffers gang up on it and take turns in attacking it from all sides, harassing it like a pack of wolves until one member can deliver a bite to the crab's vital nerve centre to paralyze it. Then they all quickly tear it to pieces.

Whether the northern puffer lays its sticky, heavy eggs on the bottom or whether it simply broadcasts them through the water, allowing them to sink by their own weight, is not definitely known. At any rate, spawning takes place during the late spring and summer, and the tiny spherical eggs hatch about four to five days after being laid. Baby puffers only a quarter of an inch long can inflate themselves, practically turning inside out to do so. Female northern puffers attain a length of almost nine and one-half inches, while males rarely exceed

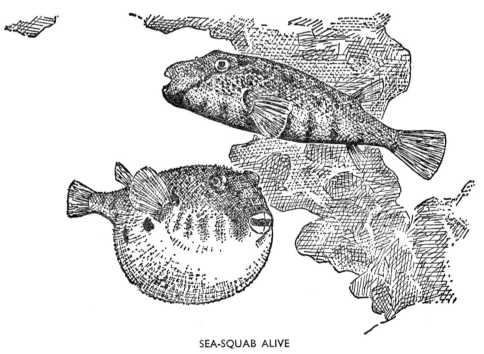

SEA-SQUAB ALIVE

When cooked the tail muscles of the northern puffer make a succulent dish known as sea-squab. Alive, in its home waters along the Atlantic coast of the United States, this fish is capable of inflating itself with air or water until it assumes a globelike shape. Its foes find it a difficult prey to take hold of.

eight and one-half. The species ranges from Maine to Florida in shallow salt waters.

For many years it was realized that the tail muscles of the puffer make delicious eating, but it was not until the Second World War that the fish was utilized to any extent for food. Now so-called "sea-squab" is a regular item in many markets, and consists of puffers' tail muscles removed from the fish.

Reluctance to use the fish commercially arose partly from the knowledge that some of its Pacific relatives are known to be deadly poisonous. It has been shown, in some of them at least, that their poison resides in the internal organs, and that if these are removed soon enough after catching, the poison does not diffuse into the muscle meat—which then can be eaten with impunity. There is only a mild poison at some seasons in the ovaries of the northern puffer, and it apparently does not diffuse out into the fish's muscles. Moreover puffers are stripped of their meat very soon after catching, so that there is never even the slightest danger from eating tasty sea-squab.

The Deadly Death Puffer, *Tetraodon hispidus*, is fatal to anyone who eats it; the unfortunate victim usually dies within five hours. The flesh of this fish contains a poisonous substance called tetrodotoxin, which causes great pain, nausea, vomiting, and diarrhoea, often accompanied by paralysis and convulsions. The toxic material seems to be concentrated in the reproductive organs, but enough of it is present in the muscles to make eating the flesh almost invariably fatal.

Fishes that cannot be eaten because they are poisonous are found principally in tropical seas. It has been estimated that there are about three hundred species of such fishes in the central Pacific, for example. Most of these are not as dangerous as the deadly death puffer and some of its relatives. Other closely related puffers from that region are perfectly edible, however; in fact they are considered delicacies! To make matters more confusing, certain kinds of fishes seem to be poisonous only at definite seasons of the year, and some species are deadly in one area, but harmless in another. The latter fact might indicate that the food consumed by the fish imparts some poisonous quality to its flesh.

But the deadly death puffer is poisonous whenever or wherever it is found—and it is widespread through the warmer parts of the Indian and Pacific Oceans from the Red Sea to the Hawaiian Islands. It also occurs in brackish or fresh waters. The deadly death puffer is a brightly and variably coloured fish, covered with yellowish or whitish spots on its back and sides and with yellow or light olive streaks on its belly. Like most other puffers it can inflate itself with air or water. It may grow to a length of twenty inches.

The Porcupine Fish, *Diodon hystrix,* is covered with numerous long spines. Ordinarily these lie close to the body, but when the fish inflates itself—like its relative the puffer—it looks like a spherical pin-cushion, all of its spines sticking straight out. These can inflict painful wounds, for they are both sharp and long—more than two inches in large specimens. Porcupine fish grow to a length of more than three feet and then appear like basketballs studded with nails, when they are blown up.

Found all over the world in tropical seas, the porcupine fish is well known to many peoples, but its life history is pretty much of a mystery. The Japanese use it for food, although it is considered poisonous in most countries. People have died from eating its flesh, which is believed to become toxic by absorbing poison from the fish's vital organs after its death. South Sea Islanders employed the spiny skins of porcupine fish in making helmets for their war dress.

The Ocean Sunfish, *Mola mola,* has a peculiar oval body, flattened from side to side, with a long narrow dorsal and anal fin projecting up and down from the posterior part of it. At first glance it seems to have no tail at all, but close examination reveals that an abbreviated, crescent-shaped one covers the whole back of the body. The fish gives the appearance of having had the rear half of its body chopped off. It swims by swinging its dorsal and anal fins back and forth, both together, and by undulating them at the same time.

Large specimens of the ocean sunfish are seen swimming or floating lazily at the surface of all the tropical seas or in temperate ones during the warmer months. They attain weights of over a ton and lengths of perhaps eleven feet. Their greyish brown skin is leathery in texture, very tough, and averages more than two inches in thickness. The interior of the fish shows specializations as peculiar as those manifested externally. For example, it has lost the usual trunk muscles present in ordinary fish, and its skeleton is so soft that it can be cut with a knife

Ocean sunfish feed on small crustaceans, jellyfish, the larvae of other fishes, and perhaps algae. Reproduction is by means of tiny, floating eggs. Larval sunfish look entirely different from adults, bearing a number of variously shaped spines. The species is not generally considered edible, although the Japanese are said to relish its liver.

A TON OF FISH

The ocean sunfish loves to take the sun, swimming lazily along the surface of warm and temperate seas. This remarkable fish may weigh as much as a ton and measure eleven feet ın length, but it is of scant value to the larders of mankind, for its flesh is leathery.

The name "Protozoa" comes from a combination of two Greek words "protos" and "zoon" meaning "first animal". While it is difficult to entertain the idea that a single cell can function as an entire organism, performing all the essential life processes of an animal, this is the case with protozoa. The 30,000 known species are divided into five main categories on the basis of the structures they possess for locomotion. Noctiluca, or nightlight, is a luminous member of the flagellate group which possess one or more whiplike hairs, or flagella, and propel themselves through the water by beating the flagella back and forth. The Ciliophora are completely covered with tiny fine hair-like structures called cilia, and move by vibrating the cilia rapidly.

See page 1645

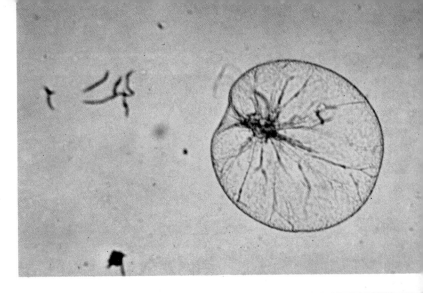

Young Suctoria have cilia and are free-swimming, but the adults replace the cilia with delicate tentacles and attach themselves permanently to inanimate objects, plants and small aquatic vertebrates. Some of the tentacles are tipped with rounded knobs that act like suction cups, catching and holding the small ciliates on which the Suctoria feed, while others are pointed to pierce the prey so that its soft parts flow through the tentacles into the cell body.

See page 1645

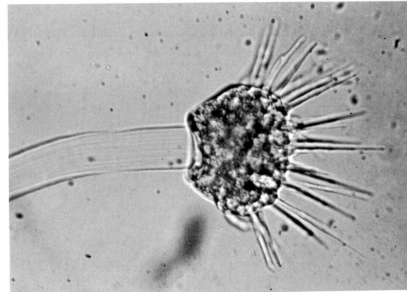

The Sporozoa possess no locomotor organelles whatsoever and are practically all parasites; a large number of invertebrates are host to the gregarines. Distinct species occur in different animals from other protozoa to man, malaria being the most serious human disease they cause. The Trypanosoma which cause sleeping sickness are flagellates, and amoebic dysentery is caused by one species of the fifth group, the Sarcodina, which move by extending part of themselves in one direction and then pulling the rest of the cell along. The 1,200 species of shell-bearing amoebae known as Foraminifera have left fossil records indicating that they have been living 500 million years.

See page 1650

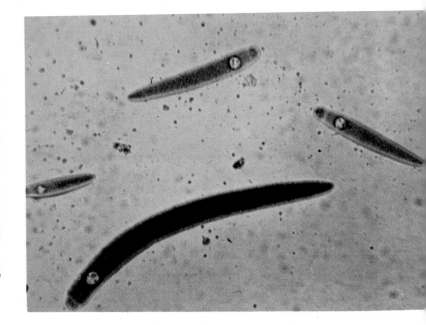

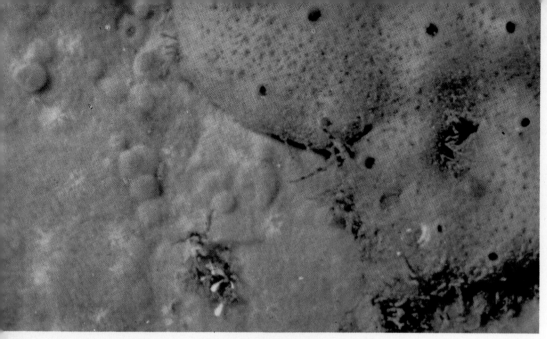

[13-10]

Sponges were long thought to be plants and their proper place in the animal king-dom was settled little more than 100 years ago. Of the some 3,000 species, one family of about 150 species lives in fresh water; the remainder are salt-water dwellers, found from low-tide limits to depths of three and one-half miles. They are classified according to their skeletons—the part most of us refer to when we say "sponge"—which they create by abstracting minerals from the water. Living sponges vary greatly in colour and form, some like the orange encrusting sponge being quite flat, and others like the more familiar "bath" sponge being more spherical. Different species often live together. See page 1656

The hermit sponge belongs to the class of sandy or silicious sponges which are by far the most abundant and include the freshwater species. While they have little or no commercial value, the silicious sponges assume a great variety of interesting forms and many are readily available for first-hand observation. A sponge begins life as a free-swimming animal, but very early finds a suitable rock, shell or other firm base to which it can attach itself. The ability of sponges to regenerate lost pieces is the basis for the extensive commercial cultivation of the "bath" sponges. See page 1660

[13-10A]

Toadfishes—Some Can Sing

THE TOADFISHES—ugly, battling scavengers—live on the bottom of tropical and temperate seas from shallow to deep water. Some haunt inlets; a few tropical species enter rivers. Coloured like the rocks and weeds amid which they dwell, they often stay in ambush till their prey draws near.

The largest toadfishes reach a length of about one and one-half feet, but the majority are less than one foot long. Some of them, because they have, on the belly, rows of luminous organs rather like shining buttons, are known as midshipmen. Many are able to produce noises by vibrating their swim bladder. Those species whose habits we know, lay adhesive eggs over which the male keeps watch.

On the east and west coasts of tropical South America and in the Caribbean Sea there are a few toadfishes (genus *Thalassophryne*) which are notorious for their poisonous spines. Two of these spines are located in the front part of the first dorsal fin, and one projects backward from each gill cover. The dorsal ones at least are hollow, with an opening near the tip, and are connected to sacs in which poisonous material is stored. The resemblance to the fangs of venomous snakes is striking.

The toadfishes and their relatives (order Haplodoci) are generally stout-bodied, with naked skins or with small scales thoroughly embedded in slime. The mouth looks savage; it is large, and armed with curved canine teeth. Pelvic fins are located well forward. There is only one family (Batrachoididae, or "froglike"), and it has about thirty species in it.

The Toadfish, *Opsanus tau,* acts as tough as it looks. Its stocky, scaleless, darkly mottled body and large, flattened, tab-covered head give it a somewhat repulsive appearance, while its capacious mouth and strong jaws, well armed with numerous blunt teeth, is set at the correct angle to make it appear most pugnacious.

Toadfish can and do inflict nasty wounds when incautiously handled; they are especially full of fight while guarding their nest. Moreover, they can survive under adverse living conditions shunned by most fishes. For example, they can withstand severe shortages of oxygen, particularly in the younger stages. They can also live out of water for several hours. If annoyed by sticks or shells, toadfish will often bite the object so hard that they can be lifted out of the water still tenaciously hanging on.

Toadfish often live in very shallow water along the shore from Maine to Florida. Such places may become very warm in summer, hence the usefulness of the fish's ability to withstand poor breathing conditions. They feed voraciously on a great variety of animals, including worms, shrimps, crabs, snails, bivalves, squid, fishes of all sorts, and offal resulting from the activities of man.

Toadfish have even turned to good account man's proclivity to litter

UGLY IN APPEARANCE AND DISPOSITION

The mouth of the toadfish is armed with many teeth, and this unpleasant-looking, mottled creature has been known to inflict extremely painful bites with them. Toadfish live close to shore, and will often use a tin can or some other man-made object as a nest; the male guards the eggs, and will fight off any intruders with great ferocity.

the world with his trash. Among their favourite nesting sites appear to be broken bottles, jugs, tin cans, boards, and old shoes—apparently anything that provides a large enough cavity—as well as more natural objects like shells and stones. These nests are diligently guarded, each by a male fish. During June and July the large, three-sixteenth-inch, amber eggs are spawned. They are spherical and adhesive, and are usually laid in a single layer on the floor or roof of the nest.

As many as seven hundred eggs may occupy one nest, such a large number being the product of more than one female. They hatch in ten to twenty-six days depending on the temperature. All this while the male carefully cleans his nest and eggs and from time to time fans them with his large pectoral fins. The young remain within the nest under the protection of their father for some time after hatching.

Toadfish spend the winter hibernating in mud. By the time they are one year old, young toadfish are about three and one-half inches long. They may grow to be fifteen inches in length, but rarely exceed one foot. In captivity toadfish sometimes become quite tame, learning not to resist handling and to be fed by hand.

The Pacific Midshipman, *Porichthys notatus*, is best known for the noises it makes, giving it the name of "singing fish". These sounds have variously been described as a humming, a resonant croak or bark, or a grunting noise that sounds like "oonk". It is agreed, however, that the fish can make itself heard for remarkable distances—at least forty to fifty feet. The sounds are produced by vibrating the swim bladder by means of special muscles.

The midshipman is an elongated fish with a rather large head, mouth, and pair of eyes. It is a dirty brown or green, and its scaleless body and head show numerous small, round luminous organs, arranged in rows. Each of these tiny light-producing regions is equipped with a minute lens. Midshipmen grow to be about fifteen inches long. During most of the year they inhabit moderately deep water along the west coast of North America from south-eastern Alaska to the southern end of Baja California. North of Point Conception they migrate into shallow water to spawn during the late spring.

Cavities underneath stones are used as nests. Sometimes these are scooped out by means of the fish's pectoral fins. Large, adhesive, pinkish eggs are laid in a single layer on the roof of the nest. Sometimes several females will spawn in a single cavity. Usually there are from two hundred to five hundred eggs, guarded faithfully by the male midshipman, who never leaves even to feed. He cleans the eggs by rubbing them, and if the nest is so located that the eggs are exposed to air during low tide, he remains below, splashing them by means of his fins. Midshipmen can live as long as eight hours out of water if kept moist.

Hatching occurs in two to three weeks, and for a month afterwards the larvae remain attached to the roof of the nest by the yolk sac. Finally, when they are about one and a quarter inches long, the young fish become free-swimming. They burrow in the sand during the day, and feed on small invertebrates at night. Adults consume larger crustaceans and other fishes.

Anglers and Batfishes—Fish That Fish for Other Fish

THE VARIOUS kinds of angler fishes and their relatives are especially interesting, because they are not only fish, but fishermen. Many of them have a spine of the first dorsal fin modified to form a lure and use it to attract prey. Usually, their bodies are stout and clumsy, with a head and mouth that are relatively enormous.

The frogfishes or fishing-frogs and their cousin, the sargassum fish, (family Antennariidae) are found in shallow, tropical salt waters around coral reefs and among seaweed, or in mid-ocean living in floating seaweed. Many of them show bizarre colour patterns and threadlike "decorations", but in all instances these seem to aid in camouflaging the fish. The largest species reaches a length of about eighteen inches and a weight of several pounds, but few antennarids are ever one foot long at maximum size, many being less than six inches.

The anglers (family Lophiidae, with perhaps a dozen species) are large, bottom-inhabiting fishes found most frequently in fairly deep water. Some species enter shallow water during the colder parts of the year. Anglers are known from the Atlantic, Pacific, and Indian Oceans. The largest species become four or more feet long.

The deep-sea anglers belong to nearly a dozen families. Approximately 120 species are known from the depths of oceans all over the world. Most of them are small, but a few reach lengths of about three and a half feet. Unlike the members of the family Lophiidae, the deep-sea anglers do not habitually lie on the bottom, but do their fishing in mid-water, fifteen hundred to fifteen thousand feet below the surface. Females are equipped with a lure, which is believed to be luminous in all cases—as indeed it would have to be in order to operate effectively in those regions of total darkness. It has been shown in a number of cases that the light is not produced by the fish itself, but by special bacteria living inside the bait.

There is a fantastic variety of styles among the fishing apparatus of deep-sea anglers. Some are short, in others the "fishing rod" is as much as three times as long as the total length of the fish. Some are tipped with simple, bulbous lures, others with weirdly branched or shaped ones, often bearing peculiar tentacles or buds. So little is known about these fish that it would be foolhardy to try to explain just what is the significance of this great variability.

Deep-sea angler males are very much smaller than females, and they never possess a lure. So entirely different are they from the females that for years they were considered to belong to entirely separate species, even different families.

In the north Atlantic, spawning occurs mostly during the summer. After hatching, the young fish live mainly in the upper layer of the ocean, feeding on small floating creatures, until they become adult-like in form and sink down into deep water.

The batfishes (family Ogcocephalidae) are among the most peculiarly shaped of all fishes. They are much depressed, that is, flattened from back to belly, and the pectoral fins extend out at an angle from broad triangular bases on either side of the head. With these two fins and the sturdy pair of pelvics underneath, a batfish can walk about the bottom, moving alternate forelimbs (pelvics) and hind limbs (pectorals) together. This "four-footed" gait, unique in fish, may be replaced by rabbitlike hops. When the fish jumps, the pectorals provide the power for the leap, and the fish makes its landing on the pelvic fins.

At least one species of batfish has been seen to angle for prey. The knoblike bait is affixed to a short stem that moves in and out like a plunger. When not in use, the mechanism is hidden inside the "fore-head" of the fish. The various batfishes inhabit the bottom of tropical seas, often in deep water. They seldom exceed one foot in length.

WALKER ON THE OCEAN FLOOR
The batfish is a fish with "feet"—its lower fins are long and sturdy, and the creature is able to walk about on them on the ocean floor, or even hop, after a fashion.

All told, there are about sixteen families in this group of salt-water fishes (order Pediculati—"little feet"). We have already had a brief picture of some of their peculiar features: these include strange pectoral fins, ribs, tail, and bony structure of the skull. The gill openings are small and are located behind the pectoral fins, not in front of them as in other fishes. In a few of the anglers, however, these openings extend in front of the base of the pectorals. Each pectoral fin is attached to a fleshy base with an elbow-like joint. This structure is so well developed in some of the antennarids (frogfishes and the like) that the fin acts somewhat like a limb, complete with "arm", "wrist", "hand", and "fingers". When present, the pelvic fins are located in front of the pectorals. Scales are present only as prickles in the skin, or are absent altogether.

The Sargassum Fish, *Histrio gibba,* lives among sargassum weed and climbs about this floating ocean plant by means of peculiar pectoral fins, so constructed that the fish can actually grasp a branch with its "fingers" and hold on to it. At the same time the pelvic fins are also employed somewhat like feet, in a shuffling manner, to aid in moving about. So well do the many fringes and tabs on the sargassum fish's head and body break up its outline, and so perfectly does its colour and pattern match that of the sargassum weed, that an individual can disappear before one's eyes as it deliberately moves about in a clump of this seaweed.

Although they rarely exceed four inches in length, sargassum fish have huge appetites and, if given the chance, will eat considerably more than their own weight in food at one time. They can swallow a fish larger than themselves because of their relatively enormous mouths and the fact that their stomachs can be stretched out of all proportion to their size. Prey is stalked—sometimes for hours on end—until approached near enough, when with a sudden dart and widely opened mouth the sargassum fish engulfs it. The fish is capable of making relatively great flying leaps, and it can also swim slowly in mid-water by utilizing the jets of water emitted from its gill openings together with the pectoral fins.

The eggs are laid in floating, gelatinous rafts that are many times as large as the fish that spawned them. They lie tightly rolled up within the ovaries, but once laid the jelly-like sheet enveloping them swells tremendously. The sargassum fish has been found in practically all tropical seas. It occasionally drifts north along with the seaweed in which it habitually lives.

The Goosefish, *Lophius americanus,* uses one of its spines as a fishing rod, complete with bait, to lure prey within reach of its great mouth. The first three spines of its dorsal fin stand apart, separated from one another; the most forward of these is located just behind the upper lip of the mouth and is equipped with an irregular, leaflike flap of skin at its tip. This lure is jerked back and forth over the mouth in a way that apparently successfully imitates the movement of small, edible creatures, because several kinds of fishes have been seen to be attracted by it—and abruptly to end their lives within the goose-fish's maw.

At first glance the goosefish appears to be "all head", and its head seems to be "all mouth". Almost one-half of the entire fish is composed of the very wide, flat head, and the body so sharply tapers down to the tail and is relatively so small that the goosefish looks like a tadpole at first glance. The enormous mouth is directed upwards, and the lower jaw projects far beyond the upper. Both jaws are lined with numerous sharp, fanglike teeth which may be an inch long in large specimens. The eyes are located on top of the head and are directed upwards. The pectoral fins arise from thick, fleshy arms instead of directly out of the body as they do in most fishes. No gill covers are present, but instead there is a small opening from the gill chamber behind each pectoral fin. Rows of fleshy tabs decorate the scaleless, slimy head and body. The colour is dark brown or black on top and dirty white underneath.

Goosefish reach lengths of three to four feet. They actively stalk their prey and also lie passively on the bottom, luring it within reach by means of their rod and bait. In either case, the creature is suddenly and completely engulfed (if not too large) by the goosefish's tremendous mouth, the mere sudden opening of which causes a strong flow of water helping to draw the prey to its fate.

The appetite of the goosefish is enormous, if not insatiable. Not only are fishes and invertebrates of all sorts consumed, but many species of sea-birds and now and then a sea-turtle are captured and eaten. One goosefish's stomach contained twenty-one flounders and a dogfish, all of marketable size; another had seventy-five herrings, and a third had seven ducks! The mass of food frequently weighs half as much as the whole fish, that is, twenty pounds or more. Sometimes goosefish swallow, or try to swallow, too large an animal and die as a result.

The range of the goosefish is along the eastern coast of North America from Newfoundland to North Carolina in shallow water and to Barbados and the Gulf of Mexico in deep water. The fish tends to come closer inshore during cold weather.

The eggs are laid in late spring and summer. They appear in floating ribbon-shaped veils of mucus that may be twenty to thirty feet long and two to three feet wide, containing hundreds of thousands of eggs about three thirty-seconds of an inch in diameter. They hatch in about four or five days; the young swim at the surface of the open sea until about an inch and a quarter long, when they take up a life among floating seaweed. Later they sink to the bottom, near or upon which they spend the rest of their lives.

The Deep-Sea Angler, *Borophryne apogon,* is one of a number of fishes that inhabit the depths of the ocean. It has a baglike body that is capable of great expansion, well-developed fins, and enormous jaws lined with many sharp teeth, some of them fanglike. These teeth are so long that the creature apparently cannot close its mouth completely. The eyes appear to be well developed. Just over the mouth is located a short, flexible projection at the tip of which is a bulbous structure carrying a complicated mass of hairlike threads. This bulb is bluish-purple, and the filaments are white, while the rest of the fish is jet black. The bulb is capable of emitting purplish light.

This small species of deep-sea angler reaches a length of somewhat more than three inches. Nevertheless it is capable of swallowing a

AFTER THE DEEP-SEA ANGLER HAS DINED

The female deep-sea angler, only three inches long, is able to swallow another fish fully her own size, after which her belly swells up enormously. The tiny fish below her is the inch-long male. He becomes permanently attached to his mate's body, a mere appendage serving to fertilize her eggs.

fish almost as long as itself or as many as three specimens, each measuring two-thirds of its length—after which its belly swells out like a balloon. So far as known, it inhabits the icy depths of the tropical eastern Pacific, but may of course be much more widely distributed, since we know so very little about the geography of deep-sea fishes. Experts believe that it uses its glowing lure to attract fishes within reach of the fearsome jaws. Since it is capable of swimming strongly, even when its stomach is bulging with food, the possibility cannot be overlooked that it also actively pursues prey, or moves about in search of suitable fish on which to use its lure.

What we have said applies only to females, for the adult males of this species start out as free-swimming fish less than an inch long with no mechanism for angling but possessing well-developed eyes, noses, and jaws. When a male comes upon a suitable female, he attaches himself to her by means of his mouth. Any part of her body seems to be satisfactory, and eventually his jaws become fused with the skin of the relatively gigantic female, only enough space remaining between the two partners for a small amount of water to enter the male's mouth, presumably to bathe the gills. Experts believe that the male's blood stream becomes connected with that of the female, and that she supplies him with nourishment through this means. For the rest of his life the male remains attached to his mate, a mere parasitic tab on her body. His only function is to fertilize the numerous eggs, about a sixty-fourth of an inch in diameter, when they are laid.

Section 5

INSECTS AND
OTHER INVERTEBRATES

———

JOHN C. PALLISTER

The Great World of the Animals
Without Backbones

HOW WE CLASSIFY ANIMALS

IF A MODERN Noah were to assemble specimens of all the kinds of animals, from the least to the greatest, and to try to allot them berths so that each would be surrounded by its next of kin, he might first try to arrange them according to size. But he would not like the resulting groups. Placing the ostrich between the kangaroo and the tuna fish just wouldn't do, nor would it seem right to place the humming-bird between the tarantula and the field mouse.

Our twentieth-century Noah would soon decide that all creatures with wings and feathers must be more closely related to one another than to any other animals. He might then try to separate all animals into large categories, such as animals that live in the water and animals that live on land. That division would seem valid as far as birds and fishes are concerned; but Noah would quickly observe that some shelled animals live in the ocean and some climb trees, while some six-legged animals, such as mosquitoes, spend the first part of their lives wriggling in the water and the last part flying in the air.

Sooner or later, he would observe that many animals have backbones, and that many more have none. If he put all creatures with backbones in one division, he would see that all of them have very complex bodies, and that they can be subdivided easily into five distinct groups: fishes, amphibians (consisting of frogs, toads, and their relatives), snakes and lizards, birds, and finally the mammals. If he looked, then, at all the animals without backbones, he would be facing a tremendous number of creatures, of such differing body formation that they have almost no points in common except that they are animals and they are spineless.

This problem that we have given our imagined Noah is a very real one to the zoologist who wants to look at animal life as a whole, and to study the habits, origins, and relationships of living creatures. Most of our methods of arranging and studying living forms have been developed within the last two hundred years. It was only about 150 years ago that the great zoologist Lamarck first classified all animals into two divisions. All those with backbones he called vertebrates; all the spineless, invertebrates.

A few years before Lamarck's work, the Swedish botanist Linnaeus had devised a set of terms for the divisions and subdivisions among both plants and animals. Let us review them here. The term for the largest division is phylum (plural, phyla). The vertebrates are considered a phylum. A phylum may be subdivided into classes. Birds form one class of the vertebrate phylum. Classes are further subdivided into orders. For example, all the perching birds are placed in one order. Each order consists of a number of families. The thrush family belongs to the perching-bird order. Families are divided into genera (singular, genus). Bluebirds form one genus of the thrush family. Finally, genera are divided into species, a classification by which, for example, we separate the Eastern from the Western blue-bird.

To take an example from the invertebrates: the Arthropoda (lobsters, spiders, insects, etc.) is a phylum, of which the insects are one class, and in this class moths and butterflies together form the Lepidoptera order. One of the largest of its 160 families is the Nymphalidae, and in this family *Vanessa* is a genus, and the Painted Lady, *Vanessa cardui*, is a species that almost everyone in Europe and the United States has seen.

THE INNUMERABLE INVERTEBRATES

In the following chapters we will consider some of the odd, interesting, or beautiful animals that make up the invertebrates. Unlike the vertebrates, these do not consist of just one phylum but of several, possibly eleven, each possessing characteristics as distinct from those of the others as from those of the vertebrates.

"Innumerable" is the word to stress in trying to think of these animals en masse. Not only do the invertebrates outnumber the verte-brates in phyla, they also exceed all mammals, birds, reptiles, amphibians, and fishes in species by about twenty-eight to one. They range in structure from a simple, microscopic globule of protoplasm, like the amoeba, to creatures of such complex and specialized formation as the lobster, the seventeen-year cicada, the sponges, the chambered nautilus, the mosquito, and the octopus.

Some of these creatures live simple, uneventful lives from beginning to end. Some live parasitically on, or in, other animals; and some of these, like the malarial parasite, may become seasoned travellers, living for a time in one kind of animal, then moving to another kind, and then to still another. Some live the early part of their lives as alarming caterpillars, and the latter part as beautiful butterflies. Obviously, only a very few species can be discussed in these pages. You will find descriptions here of those that are typical, or lead especially exciting lives, or have some known relation to man. All of the phyla will be discussed to some extent.

The First Animals

ANIMALS OF BUT A SINGLE CELL

PROTOZOA are the first or earliest creatures in the animal kingdom in the sense that they have the simplest kinds of bodies. These minute animals do not have a head, heart, stomach, legs, or any of the other parts we usually find in an animal. The protozoan's entire body consists of just one cell. With this single cell, the protozoan absorbs its food, moves about, divides itself to form new individuals, and may even develop a covering.

Protozoa are everywhere, on land, in the sea, and in the air, but chiefly near the surface of shallow water, either salt or fresh. Stagnant water teems with them. Most of the species are too small to be visible to the naked eye, and only a few can be seen without a hand lens. They are so transparent that you look right through them, seeing only a speck of jelly-like material, called protoplasm. It takes a medium-powered, compound or binocular microscope to reveal these beautiful little creatures belonging to the phylum Protozoa.

The Amoeba. One-celled though they may be, the animals belonging to the genus *Amoeba* are unique in that they are constantly changing shape. The best way to observe some of them is to place a drop of stagnant water on a glass slide. If naturally stagnant water is not easily available to you, soak a little grass in a jar of water at room temperature for a few days. Place a thin cover glass over the water to compress it into a thin layer. This is necessary because the focal depth of a microscope is extremely shallow, and gets rapidly shallower as the magnification is increased. However, in order to gain a little more room for activity in the water, you will find it helpful to support the cover glass by a few fibres of cotton or some hairs from your head placed beside the drop of water.

Adjust the focus and the light to get the clearest possible view, and you will soon be gazing at the strange and intriguing world known only to the microscopist. If you are fortunate, a disc of transparent jelly on the slide will start to bulge on one side. You will see the bulge extend farther and farther, until, suddenly, the entire blob will seemingly flow into this extended arm, or pseudopod. Meanwhile, other pseudopods will have reached out from the blob. The main mass will finally flow into one of these, as it did before. This is the amoeba's method of travel.

You may notice a darker spot somewhere near the centre of the mass. It is the all-important nucleus, the spot of essential life within the protoplasm. And, somewhere, you should observe one or more oily spots known as the contractile vacuoles, small cavities which contract and expand at more or less rhythmical or regular intervals. There may be other roundish spots, the food vacuoles; these are fragments of food which the amoeba has surrounded and is assimilating. When the edible parts have been dissolved, the animal discards the remainder by the simple process of flowing on and leaving it behind.

——How Amoebae Separate and Unite. There comes a time when two pseudopods form, seemingly of equal importance, and usually on

The freshwater hydra is a tiny solitary animal which moves about, but marine species live in colonies attached to logs, shells and bits of debris in shallow water. While the colonies may vary in size from less than one inch to more than a foot, the individual hydroid polyps of most species are microscopic. The colonies vary in complexity of structure and polyp function but in their simplest form they are composed of a base and stem which are continuous with the polyps and through which digested food circulates. The polyps are of two kinds, the hydranth which feeds the colony, and the gonangium which reproduces it.

See page 1662

[13-11]

[13-11A]

The sexual reproduction phase of marine hydroid colonies produces minute jellyfish, or medusae, which carry out this function, and a large majority of jellyfish pass through a hydroid stage in the course of their development. Polyorchis, the red-eyed jellyfish of the Pacific Coast, is one of the few which do not. Jellyfish can swim feebly but for the most part float on the surface at the mercy of the waves and tides. The many species offer a wide variety of shapes, sizes and colours, but all have the dangling, stinger-equipped tentacles for securing food and repelling intruders. As the sting is poisonous and has a paralyzing effect, the larger species can be a serious menace to bathers.

See page 1662

[13-12]

Sea anemones do not have a medusa form but exist only as polyps which may be solitary or make up a colony formation. While the anemones attach themselves firmly to suitable objects (one species rides the back of the hermit crab) they can creep about slowly on their flat bases. Members of the delicately coloured Sagartia family have long tentacles arranged in definite rows. These small, slender animals are found near the low-tide mark in all the waters of the world.   *See page 1669*

The large green anemone inhabits the tide pools of the West Coast of America, and owes the drab green colour of its body stalk to small algae which actually live in its tissues. The mouth is the only body opening and a constant current of water flows into one part providing the animal with oxygen, and passes out another part carrying away waste products and reproductive cells. While anemones usually feed themselves with their brightly coloured tentacles, the muscular mouth can gape wide and snap shut on unsuspecting prey. When disturbed or exposed to air by receding tides, anemones pull in their tentacles and become lumpy stumps.   *See page 1669*

[13-12A]

opposite sides of the animal. The protoplasm is now flowing into both of these arms. The amoeba is increasing in length and is beginning to shrink in the middle. The nucleus has divided, one-half to each part. Soon, the two parts separate and flow off in opposite directions. This method of reproduction, known as binary fission, is followed by the Protozoa.

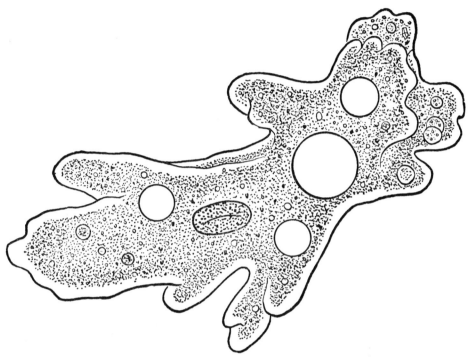

THE LOWLY AMOEBA, MOST PRIMITIVE OF ANIMALS

This tiny speck of protoplasm, endowed with the spark of life, flows slowly through its little world. It moves by pushing out a part of itself and pulling the rest along. In its travels, it engulfs everything smaller than itself. As it passes on, it absorbs whatever is food; whatever is not food it leaves behind.

Sometimes two amoebae unite. They meet and, after a moment of hesitation, either slide along past each other or flow into each other.

For all its apparent fragility, the amoeba is a durable animal. When it finds conditions unfavourable for an active life, it prepares for hard times. First, it assumes a spherical shape by pulling in all its pseudopods. Then, it thickens and toughens the wall which surrounds its one-celled self. In this condition, when the pool in which it has been living dries up, the amoeba is picked up by the wind and carried away, to lodge, perhaps on a mountain peak, or perhaps on the side of a shed. There it can linger until rains come to carry it to another stream, pond, or puddle. Then, its cystlike wall is broken, and the amoeba resumes activity once again.

If the amoeba we have been watching has pseudopods that are rounded at the ends, it is probably *Amoeba proteus*. *Amoeba quarta* has short, sharp pseudopods. Another amoeba that you might find in your drop of stagnant water has pseudopods so short and round that the creature appears to have a roughly scalloped edge. It is called *Amoeba verrucosa*.

Amoebae That Live in Other Animals. Most amoebae live in water, salt or fresh; a few live in damp earth. One whole family, comprising many species, lives in the digestive tracts of other animals. Of these, one species makes its home in cockroaches. Another species, *Entamoeba coli*, lives harmlessly in the human colon; but the species called *Entamoeba histolytica* causes the dangerous illness, amoebic dysentery.

FORAMINIFERA

This large group of protozoans with the long name is interesting for two reasons. Their first claim to distinction is that within the limits of their one-celled bodies these creatures have developed strange or beautiful shapes. There are about twelve hundred species of Foraminifera, each as queer or as exquisite as the others. They are so tiny that you can study them only under a microscope, but you will find them well worth all the time you spend on them. Secondly, they have lived through so many geological ages that today, in many parts of the world, their tiny skeletons form important parts of our landscape. They compose the chalk cliffs of England, and they are present in many of the limestone ridges of North America. They are also a large part of the soft muck that we find at the water's edge at low tide.

It is hard to believe that the great city of Paris is indebted to these obscure animals. In the region of the city, there is a large bed of limestone. It is composed almost entirely of the shells of the Foraminifera genus *Miliolina*, and is hundreds of millions of years old. Many of the buildings of Paris are made of this stone; in it you can see the minute remains of Miliolinas with the aid of a lens.

Most of the Foraminifera build shells of lime or silica. These shells are perforated with many small and some larger holes (called foramen, from which we get the name Foraminifera). Through these holes stream the pseudopods, not lumpy or clubbed like those of the amoebae, but long, slender, very delicate, sometimes branching, and often inter-laced into a net or web. And yet, for all this extraordinary outward form, within its shell the tiny creature remains a simple, one-celled mass of protoplasm.

Most Foraminifera are ocean dwellers. A few live in fresh water; a very few species have been found in damp earth. Certain species live on, or near, the surface of the ocean and are called "pelagic" forms. Many of these create complicated and spiny shells. In the *Globigerina* species, the individual, while growing, builds a series of adjoining shell-chambers, all connected by a passage through which the protoplasm is united in a single cell. As these pelagic Foraminifera die, their shells sink to the bottom of the ocean, forming a layer of grey mud there. This mud is called "globigerina ooze", although it might be more accurate to call it "foraminifera ooze".

Most of these creatures live only on the beds of deep seas, and these are called "abyssal". Those at the greatest depths have shells of silica, more durable stuff than the lime used by their surface relatives.

Foraminifera have been living on this earth for some 500,000,000 years, ever since the days geologists describe as the Cambrian period, the earliest subdivision of the Paleozoic era. Their fossils have been found all over the world, but chiefly in the North Temperate Zone. Many of the ancient species were much larger than any of those living today; others were only about the size of a shilling.

It is not their size, however, that is significant, but their great numbers. The stupendous quantities of Foraminifera that compose our familiar limestone ridges and chalk cliffs are beyond human comprehension. Those living today are almost equally numberless.

SOME COMMON FRESHWATER PROTOZOA

Euglena. Often enough, as you stand beside a small pond or walk beside a roadside ditch, you will notice that the water appears greenish. A drop of that water examined under a microscope is almost sure to show, among many other things, a specimen of the protozoan *Euglena viridis*. It does not look at all like the amoebae that are likely to be living in the same drop of water. It is greenish and spindle-shaped, and at its blunt end you can distinguish what looks like a short, wavy hair. This hairlike tail is called a flagellum (plural, flagella). Its tiny possessor lashes it back and forth to propel itself through the water.

Inside the body of *Euglena viridis*, and not far from the base of the flagellum, you will notice a bright-red spot, called a stigma. This is believed to be a light-detecting organ, the very simplest suggestion of a primitive eye.

The green colouring of this animal is caused by the vegetable pigment, chlorophyll, together with a starchlike material called paramylum. This little green creature has the plantlike ability to decompose the carbon dioxide in water, assimilating the carbon and releasing the oxygen. However, it also possesses the animal characteristic of sweeping food into a mouthlike opening with its flagellum.

Volvox globator, found in ponds, looks like a small, green jelly-ball, but is actually composed of thousands of individuals. As the ball ages, subcolonies, called daughter colonies, form inside it. Eventually, the ball breaks, the daughter colonies separate, grow, and develop daughter colonies of their own. The ball appears to move through the water by the co-ordinated action of the flagella of its members, a faint presage of the beginning of many-celled life.

PROTOZOA THAT MAKE THEIR HOMES
IN OTHER ANIMALS

Quite a number of protozoan species live as parasites in the bodies of other animals, both vertebrate and invertebrate. We have already mentioned two *Amoeba* species parasitic on man, one dangerous and one harmless. The majority of the protozoa parasites apparently do their hosts no harm, but a few are deadly, at least to some of their hosts.

Among these deadly parasites are the species of *Trypanosoma*, one of which, *Trypanosoma gambiense*, causes the fatal African sleeping sickness in man. A slender little creature, it lives harmlessly in the blood of African antelopes. When the tsetse fly sucks the blood of an infested antelope, the trypanosome is transferred to the insect's body, where it multiplies rapidly and peacefully in the insect's salivary juices. When the fly bites a man the trypanosomes enter his bloodstream with the fly's saliva. There they wreak great havoc, first poisoning the victim's blood with their waste products, causing fever, then entering the cerebrospinal fluid, causing loss of consciousness and death.

Other species of *Trypanosoma* cause sickness and death in horses and cattle in Africa and Asia. They all lead complicated lives in a series of hosts and are conveyed to the domestic animals by flies. Species of a related genus, *Leishmania*, also cause some damage to man and other vertebrate animals. "Kala azar", a human disease common in Asia Minor is inflicted by *Leishmania donovani*.

The three malarial Protozoa, *Plasmodium malariae*, *Plasmodium vivax*, and *Plasmodium falciparum*, are credited with destroying as large a population as the atomic bomb now threatens. Fortunately, man has been able, with the help of science, to arrest these deadly malaria Protozoa.

THE HIGHEST TYPE OF PROTOZOA—CILIOPHORA

This large group of some three thousand species presents an amazing variety of shapes and forms. Some are ball-shaped; some look like fishes, or eels. Some resemble bells; some, flowers or seed pods. Some look like miniature monsters. But all have one characteristic in common —each one wears tiny, fine, hairlike structures, called cilia. Some are so thoroughly covered with cilia that they present a furry appearance. Ciliophora cannot push parts of themselves out to make pseudopods as the amoebae do, but some of the species can vibrate their cilia rapidly enough to propel themselves through the water. A very few lose their cilia when they mature, but most species retain them throughout their lives.

Ciliophora are the most highly organized of the Protozoa, for they possess a definite place for taking in food, and an exit for excrement. Their cilia may be highly specialized: some providing locomotion, some bringing food to the mouth, some protecting the animals from attack. Ciliophora live in salt and fresh water, in stagnant pools, and sluggish streams. At certain times most of them encase themselves in a horny covering, so that they can live in dry places or be carried by the winds to new locations.

The Protozoan That Looks Like a Slipper: *Paramecium.* Another protozoan that you are almost sure to see in a drop of stagnant water is one of the slipper animalcules, probably *Paramecium caudatum.* It is

larger than most of its companions, being about a quarter of a millimetre in length, and shaped somewhat like a heel-less slipper, rounded
at the front end and pointed at the back. Along the under-surface it
has a groove, called the buccal groove, corresponding to the mouth of
higher animals. This leads to an opening, called the gullet, which ends
within the protoplasmic interior of the animal.

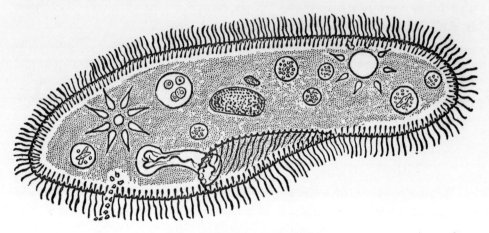

THE ROLLICKING PARAMECIUM

Unlike the plodding amoeba, the paramecium dashes about its microscopic world, propelled by vibrating cilia (hairlike growths) which cover its entire body. On one side it has
a small depression, which is a primitive mouth. The cilia around this depression sweep in
food. The paramecium is sometimes called the slipper animalcule.

The surface of this *Paramecium* is covered with lengthwise rows
of tiny cilia. By vibrating these, the creature is not only able to travel,
but also to use those along the buccal groove for bringing a constant
supply of food to the gullet.

When the animal is disturbed, it suddenly shoots out long, delicate
threads. When it is at rest, these threads lie coiled, each in its own
sac, a great many such sacs being embedded in the animal's surface.

The Cone-shaped Protozoan: *Stentor*. From plants in your
aquarium, or from small, still ponds, you may be able to collect samples
of the interesting *Stentor polymorphus*. This cone-shaped animal lives
with its small end firmly fastened to the underwater stem or leaf of a
plant. You may be able to see a *Stentor* with your unaided eye, for
they often grow to be more than one millimetre in length. Sometimes
they are green with the plants called algae, but usually they are
colourless.

Under a microscope you will be able to see a row of very fine cilia growing around the edge of the animal's wide upper end. The vibrations of these cilia bring to the mouth of the gullet, which is near one side of the upper end, all sorts of other animals small enough for *Stentor* to eat.

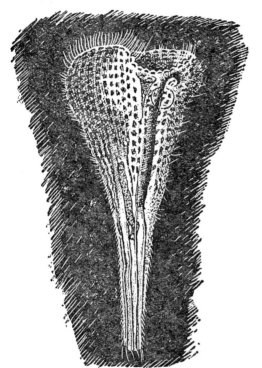

STENTOR—A VASE-SHAPED ANIMALCULE

Stiff-stemmed stentor stands at attention in its little drop of water. Some stentors are blue and some are green, but many are colourless; a number are large enough to be seen by the naked eye. Stentors usually live in colonies, attached to some solid object. But many of them can swim and, when one does, It contracts its funnel-shaped body into an oval lump.

The Cell with a Stem: *Vorticella. Vorticella campanula* is even more astounding than *Stentor*. It fastens its short, bell-shaped body to a water plant by means of a long, slender stem, which it is able to stretch or contract. When the creature is feeding, this stem is extended to its utmost, and the body sways like a flower in the breeze. The animal vibrates the cilia around its thickened edge rapidly in order to sweep the food within reach of its gullet.

Perhaps you may see more than one of these long-stemmed beauties, a garden of them, under the lens of your microscope, with cilia vibrating as they sway. They do not move in unison; each individual sways to its own rhythm. But jar the microscope or tap the slide, and fear invades the little group. All activity ceases instantly. The stems are retracted, the cilia are stilled, and the *Vorticellae* lie close to the bottom.

Not for long, however. First one extends its stem to resume operations, then another, followed closely by the others, each anxious to share in the food floating by.

VORTICELLA—A LONG-STEMMED ANIMAL VASE
A microscopic cup, fringed with cilia, waves on a long, slender stem. The stem is fastened to a rock or a piece of wood in the water. The vibrating cilia sweep food into the cup. When disturbed, the little animal stops waving its cilia, retracts its stem closer to its base, and rests motionless until the danger has passed.

The Sociable Cell: *Zoothamnium.* Some of the Ciliophora live in true colonies. Instead of each animal's attaching its stem separately to some plant or other object, a number of individuals may be attached together as a branched, treelike structure, often of striking form. *Zoothamnium* exhibits this neighbourly habit very beautifully. From a central trunk numerous branches fork out, sometimes dividing again. Dozens of little creatures nod and sway from the ends of these branches.

They live in fresh and in salt water, fastened to plants or to animals.

Zoothamnium arbuscula is one that you may find on plants in fresh water. Its colonies are sometimes a quarter of an inch high.

Protozoan with a Snout: *Didinium.* A violent little Ciliophora, familiarly known as the "water bear", is *Didinium nasutum.* It has a small, snoutlike apparatus which it can push out or pull in, and which is surrounded by a fringe of whisker-like cilia. It is not too common, but occasionally you may see one on your slide, rushing madly about, seeking a *Paramecium.* Finding one, it fastens its snout upon the victim and pulls it bodily into itself.

THE MANY-CELLED ANIMALS

All the one-celled animals in the world are contained in the one phylum, the Protozoa. The many-celled animals, having much more material with which to work, developed in widely different directions, so that they form several phyla. Nevertheless, they all start life in the same fashion, as a single-celled egg. This cell divides again and again to form other cells, amounting to many millions in the higher animals. The new cells specialize, and in this way form the various organs and tissues that make up a body.

An essential physical requirement for every animal is a place where it can hold and assimilate its food. So, from the lowest to the highest types, the many-celled animal is basically a tube into which food can be taken and digested, and from which waste can be discharged. This tube must have at least two layers, or coats, of cells—an inner layer to do the digestive work and an outer coat for protection.

Between these two layers are the cells from which all the other activities of the animal will develop—the muscular system, the reproductive organs, systems for obtaining oxygen and circulating blood, the organs of nervous control, and the organs of sense. The lower the animal, the less specialization in its cell composition and function, and the fewer and simpler its organs.

We will examine the invertebrates in the order of their complexity, as nearly as possible, beginning with the simplest. Many of the phyla show an approximately equal degree of organisation, however.

The Sponges—
Animals That Grow Like Plants

THE HUMBLE sponge with which you clean yourself or your car is the skeleton, or part of the skeleton, of a member of the odd and isolated Porifera phylum. Many phyla have members that resemble some in a lower group, but the sponges have no close relatives. It is supposed that they have developed from a group of Protozoa of which we know no examples; and none of the higher phyla appear to have evolved from the Porifera.

Sponges are water animals and, except for one small, freshwater family, are found in the sea. They tend to live fused together in colonies, where they look very much like plants or many-branched trees.

The immature, or larval, sponge can swim about. In the course of its swimming, it soon finds a rock, shell, or other firm base to which it can attach itself. After it becomes adult it cannot move. An adult sponge has no tentacles or legs, no muscles, no respiratory organs, no sense organs.

Most sponges have a cylindrical body. Pores or openings in the body wall admit water, which brings food and oxygen to a central cavity. In fact, Porifera, the name of the phylum, means "pore bearers". A large opening at one end of the body lets out the water and the waste the animal has picked up. The sponge feeds on minute animals and plants. Between its cavity and its body wall lie gelatinous cells that are able to abstract minerals from the sea water and to build up the skeletons with which we are familiar.

Sponges are classified according to the composition of their skeletons. Some create skeletons of calcium carbonate; some of a beautiful, glassy silicate. Some use a non-glassy silicate combined with a horny, fibrous material called spongin. Others compose their skeletons entirely of the elastic spongin, and furnish the commercial sponges that are so useful.

Some sponges, instead of being cylindrical or vase-shaped, are more or less flattened. These spread out on a supporting rock, much as the plants called lichens might spread on a tree trunk. Others are hemispherical in shape.

All are alike in that they take water in through the pores of the outer surface, circulate it through the tubular structure of the sponge, and pass it out through one or more openings after the food has been absorbed from it.

Scientists have described about three thousand species of sponges. The few that we find in fresh water are rather small and insignificant. They have no commercial value, but are interesting to the student.

Look at the under-side of a floating log or plank that has been in the water for some time, and you will probably see masses of the

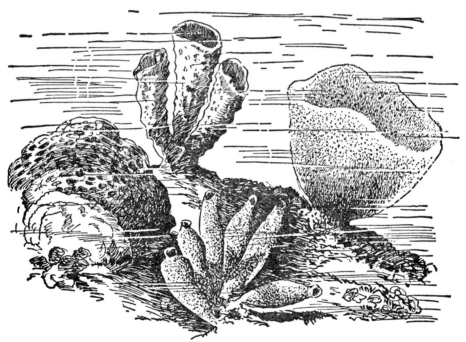

SPONGES—NATURAL WASHCLOTHS

From prehistoric days the skeletons of some sponges have been used by people as washcloths. Not all sponges, however, have the right kind of skeleton for this purpose. These animals grow in many different shapes, colours, and sizes; all but one small family of sponges live in salt water.

greenish *Spongilla* species. Turn the log back again after the short time needed for your observations, for the sponge cannot live out of water. Other freshwater sponges live on sunken logs, stones, and even on leaves lying on the bottom of some shallow pool.

We find most of the species, however, in the warmer sea waters, where the rocky bottom, providing firm bases, comes near to the surface, and where the ocean currents sweep over these rocks, bringing food.

HOW WE USE SPONGES

From the beginning of history, man has used sponges for many purposes. Undoubtedly, prehistoric man used them too.

Tribes living close to the sea collected specimens that had drifted ashore and used their surplus for barter with friendly inland tribes. The ancient Greeks used sponges not only for bathing and for scrubbing their floors and furniture, but as padding in their shields and armour. The Romans used them as mops and as paint brushes. One of the unusual uses to which sponges were put in ancient times was as drinking cups. The sponge was dipped into liquid and then squeezed into the drinker's upturned mouth. Today, we use sponges in many ways, washing cars, cleaning our homes, applying shoe polish, and even for patting on face cream (the tough spongin fibres wear better and feel better on the skin than rubber or plastic applicators).

SPONGE FISHING, A FASCINATING INDUSTRY AND SPORT

Millions of sponges are sold annually, making sponge fishing a great industry in many places that border on the sea. One of the world's finest sponge-fishing grounds lies off the Florida coast, in the Gulf of Mexico. The gathering of the high-quality bath sponges found here furnishes a livelihood to many people. In this area, Tarpon Springs, Florida, is the main port for the sponge-fishing boats from which divers descend to cut the sponges from their rocky bases.

The living bath sponge, when brought up from the bottom of the sea, has a dark, leathery covering. When cut open, it looks like a piece of raw liver. The spongin fibres are invisible in this mass of slimy protoplasm that bears not the slightest resemblance to the finished bath sponge.

As soon as the sponges are received on board, they are given a preliminary cleaning to remove rough dirt, then hung from the boat's rigging until the protoplasm decays. A sponge boat upwind can be smelled for a considerable distance beyond its visibility. The exploring scientist who goes out with a sponge fleet to study fresh specimens is likely to find the odour of the decaying ones unbearable.

When the boat docks, the sponges are washed and sorted according to their size and quality. Then they are strung up on a cord for inspection by the wholesaler. Before they are sold to the trade, the sponges are pounded with mallets to break up any solid material, such as shell-fish, that may be buried inside. After a second washing, they are trimmed to attractive shapes. Since the sponges are highly elastic, quantities of them can be pressed into bales for economy in shipping.

Sponge fishing is sometimes carried on in shallow waters, usually by two men, one who rows, and another who watches the bottom of the ocean through a water telescope. This contrivance is simply a bucket with the bottom replaced by a sheet of glass, or a tube of metal or wood with glass cemented into one end. When the fisherman spots a sponge that looks marketable, he pulls it from its support with a hook fastened to a long stick.

HORNY SPONGES

The bath sponges and most others of commercial value belong in a group called horny sponges because of the horny consistency of their spongin skeleton. One of these, called the Elephant-ear Sponge, although it is shaped more like a broad-mouthed urn, makes its home in the Mediterranean Sea. A very large sponge, it is cut into several pieces for marketing. It is used for many purposes, but particularly in the pottery trades.

CALCAREOUS SPONGES

Of the three thousand species of sponges, the majority have no commercial value because their skeletons are of hard consistency, being made up of calcareous or silicious little spikes instead of the elastic spongin. Calcareous sponges, which might be best defined as hard-shelled, limey sponges, are of various shapes and are often attached to piles or wharves. Frequently, several species will be found growing together. Many are small and bristle with calcareous deposits. They are the most common sponges in temperate sea waters.

Sycon ciliatum, which makes its home in cooler waters, consists of stubby, finger-like protuberances standing erect on a heavier base. Older specimens frequently look like a cluster of hands, with the fingers all pointing upward. There are many other species of *Sycon* scattered throughout the salt waters of the world.

SILICIOUS SPONGES

The silicious sponges, which we might in everyday language call sandy sponges, are also numerous in species. They are not useful, but many are breath-taking to see. Perhaps the most beautiful are the Venus Flower Baskers of the genus *Euplectella*. These are cylindrical tubes, six to twelve inches long, and about one to two inches in diameter. Beautiful to look at, they are unpleasant to handle, for, even through the surrounding protoplasmic material, the supporting spikelets can be felt, slightly pricking the fingers.

The remarkable beauty of this sponge is revealed only when the protoplasmic material has been removed and the skeleton washed. Gleaming white, the delicate filigree tracery appears so fragile that one fears to touch it. These sponges are extraordinarily strong, however, for nearly perfect ones are sometimes washed up on beaches, although one would think they might be pounded to bits by the waves before reaching shore.

Another genus of the glassy silicious spicules, *Staurocalyptus*, is usually urn-shaped. Protruding through the protoplasmic substance in some species are long, fine filaments of glass. The genus *Microciona* has numerous, finger-like elongations arising from one or more trunk-like bases.

Hydras, Jellyfishes, Sea Anemones, and Corals—Weird and Beautiful

THE COELENTERATA are a colourful group of water-dwelling animals. Of the ten thousand species, some live in colonies, some as free-swimming individuals. In all species, the mouth is in the centre, and the body is arranged symmetrically around the mouth.

The coelenterates differ from the sponges in having no pores in their bodies. They do, however, possess a central body cavity of some sort, and it is from this cavity that the phylum receives its name. Coelenterata comes from two meaningful words of ancient origin, *coel*, meaning "hollow", and *enteron*, meaning "intestine", and referring to the central cavity. This cavity, which serves as the stomach, has only one opening to the outside. Through this opening the animal takes in water bearing food. The water is circulated, so that the food may be gathered, not as in the sponges by means of ciliated cells, but usually through the pulsating action, or the waving, of the tentacles surrounding the mouth.

The species vary in size from organisms so tiny they are scarcely visible, to some larger organisms of considerable size. Some of the groups secrete carbonate of lime, a hard substance, which forms a supporting skeleton. These are the Stony Corals. Others have a horny secretion and are sometimes called the Black Corals. When the animal dies, its skeleton is left as a rocklike mass on which other coral animals continue to live and build.

Four classes make up the Coelenterata: freshwater polyps, or Hydrariae, and some of the jellyfishes (Hydrozoa), large jellyfishes (Scyphozoa), sea anemones and stony corals (Anthozoa), and the jellyfishes known as comb jellies (Ctenophora).

1661

HYDRAS AND A FEW JELLYFISHES

The Freshwater Hydra, *Hydra,* is one of the simplest forms of the class called Hydrozoa. You will sometimes find it in abundance in roadside ditches and small stagnant pools. Sometimes, however, you can look in all the usual places without finding any.

The hydra is a little creature about half an inch high. It consists of a tiny stem from the top of which reach out six tentacles, which can be extended for a moderate distance or pulled in close to the stem at the will of the animal. An opening, centrally located at the bases of these tentacles, and leading into the interior of the stem, serves as the mouth. The stem is attached to a firm base by means of a sticky substance. The attachment is not permanent, for the hydra frequently wishes to move, and does so by simply detaching itself and floating off.

The hydra has an amusing way of travelling. It goes places by means of a series of somersaults, and looks very much like a small boy turning handsprings. It is aided in these somersaults by its tentacles, which act like hands. Reaching a favourable new location, the hydra again attaches itself to a base, expands its tentacles, and waits for a passing morsel in the shape of a smaller animal. The unsuspecting victim, touching one of the tentacles, is stunned by the tiny, poisonous threads which shoot out from cells along these tentacles. The hydra then closes its tentacles upon the helpless victim, using them to work the animal toward its waiting mouth.

If you watch a hydra with the aid of a lens, and happen to be fortunate, you will see a bulge forming on the side of its stem. The bulge develops, becoming larger and larger, until it appears to be a little hydra. And that is exactly what this growth is. The bud soon separates from its parent and swims off on its own, an entirely new creature. This fascinating little drama is called reproduction by budding. The hydra also reproduces by means of eggs, which, when ripe, are expelled from the side of its stem. When fertilized by a swimming sperm from another hydra, the egg develops into a new creature.

The name hydra, which is actually no more than the old Greek word for "water serpent", was given to this animal because of its ability to replace parts which may become injured. This name goes all the way back to the ancient Greek myth about a great serpentine monster, the Hydra, which had nine heads. When one of its heads

[13-13]

The 1,200-mile-long Great Barrier Reef off the north-east coast of Australia and the many coral islands or atolls of the Pacific Ocean are the work of countless generations of tiny stony coral polyps. These polyps secrete a skeleton of calcereous material in the form of cells into which they can withdraw for safety. As one colony dies another builds on top of it, as is illustrated in this underwater photograph taken at Heron Island in the Reef. Present day reefs are estimated to grow at rates varying from two-tenths to seven and eight-tenths of an inch a year. The closely related species of the more temperate waters seldom produce such massive structures.

See page 1668

[13-13A]

Almost all of the more than 5,000 species of corals secrete some sort of skeleton—calcereous, limy or horny—and like the sponges it is by their skeletons most of us know them. The Gorgonia family secretes horny material, one species producing long slender, slightly branching arms, but the majority constructing the flat sea fans common to the shallow waters of the West Indies and warmer Atlantic Ocean regions. All corals are marine animals, a few species inhabiting depths of 3,000 feet. They vary in colour from pure white through shades of yellow and orange to a deep red which is almost purple.

See page 1668

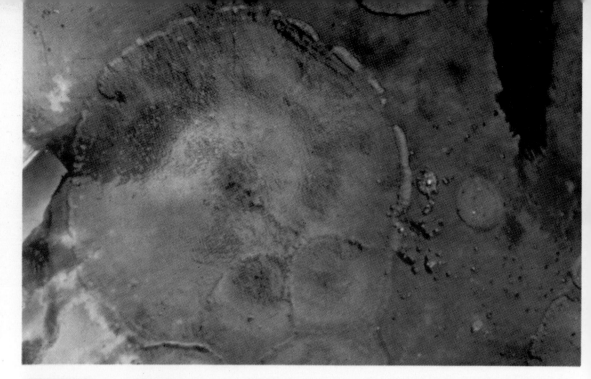

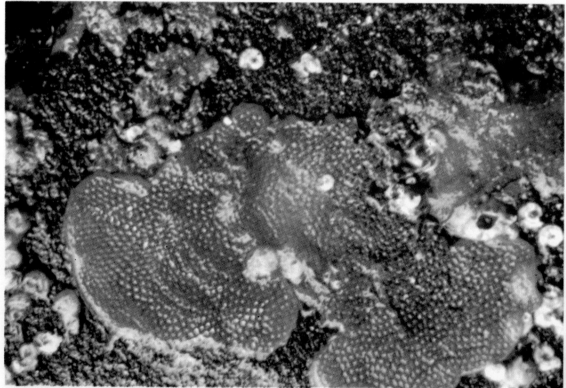

[13-14, 14A]

The Bryozoa colonies are also composed of thousands of tiny animals, but these have more differentiated body tissues and organs, and represent a step up the long ladder of biological development. Many individuals often lead a life somewhat independent of their closely attached neighbours. While the colonies of some species look so much like plants with stems and leaves that they are collected by amateurs as seaweed, others known as encrusting Bryozoans spread out flat on underwater stones, logs, piles and seaweed. Of the more than 3,000 species, less than 50 live in fresh water; the variously coloured sea-dwellers range from tide level to depths of 18,000 feet. See page 1673 was cut off, two new ones immediately grew in its place. Eventually, the monster was slain by Hercules.

The little freshwater hydras of our real-life world are found in several colours. Green ones usually belong to the genus *Chlorohydra*. Their green colour is largely caused by algae in the outer part of the body. Brown hydras belong to the genus *Pelmatohydra*, and the pinkish species to *Hydra* proper.

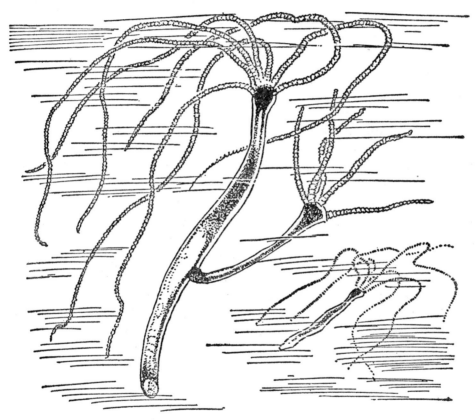

FRESHWATER HYDRAS TRAVEL BY SOMERSAULTS

Yellowish or brownish little fellows, freshwater hydras are rarely more than half an inch long. Their slender tentacles act as legs to carry them about in a tumbling fashion, or as arms to bring food to the mouth in the centre. They possess a stinging organ with which they can kill or paralyse their prey.

Obelia is a close relative of the hydra. It is, in fact, a hydroid colony or group of hydra-like animals living together and forming minute treelike structures. They appear as a filmy, oceanic growth on old logs or debris, branching and spreading and reaching heights of less than an inch in some species, while in others, a foot may be the maximum size. *Obelia* reproduces mainly by budding.

The Portuguese Man-of-war, *Physalia pelagica,* or one of its close relatives, is a startling sight for the ocean traveller who visits the warmer seas or the Gulf Stream for the first time. To see a flotilla of these purple balloons sailing on the sea far from land is an experience long to be remembered. Suddenly, at the approach of a ship, they may sink below the waves and disappear, to arise again at a later time. The animal, or perhaps we should say animals, for the Portuguese man-of-war is also a hydroid colony, can deflate the balloon apparatus through a valve in the top, or inflate it by means of a self-generated gas.

This six-inch balloon, or bladder, as it may be called, is only part of this colourful animal, for streaming down from its under-side are masses of fine tentacles. Some are quite short, others may reach a length of forty feet or more. They may stretch out straight or retract and coil up like a wire spring. Situated along the tentacles are stinging cells which can hurt you as badly as the sting of any bee or wasp. Swimmers coming in contact with even a single thread of these trailing streamers suffer indescribable agony. Wherever a tentacle touches human flesh, a red welt is raised like that left by the lash of a whip.

The animal secures its food by means of these paralysing, stinging cells, easily killing fish of considerable size. Strange to say, a few sea-dwelling animals have been able to adapt themselves to the stinging cells, and live happily amid the tentacles, protected from their enemies.

Portuguese men-of-war are carried north by the Gulf Stream and are frequently washed ashore along the Atlantic coast of the United States. The beaches of Florida are often covered with them. The gas-filled balloons quickly dry in the hot sun, and, if stepped on when dry, explode with a loud pop, much to the delight of small boys, as well as some of the larger ones. But beware of the purplish tentacles along the sands, for even after the animal is dead the tentacles retain their nettling properties for a considerable time. There are a number of other Coelenterata that have inflatable bladders, but none as spectacular as the Portuguese man-of-war.

Velella lata is a close relative. It is much smaller, and its tentacles are much shorter. Unlike the Portuguese man-of-war, it does not have a large bladder. It looks very much like a small, dark-blue boat with a clear, transparent sail to drive it along before the wind, over the wide waters of the Pacific, from Vancouver, Canada, to Central America.

Velella mutica, another near relative, makes its home along the

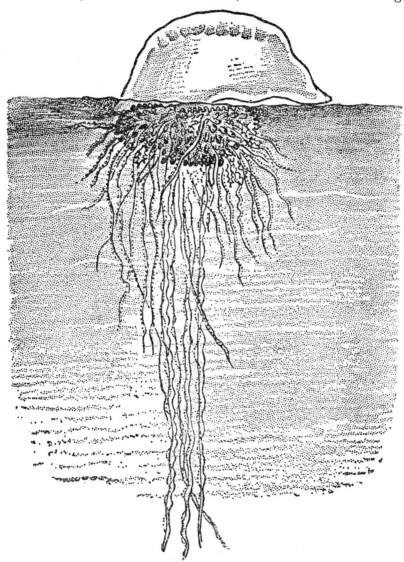

PORTUGUESE MAN-OF-WAR—A SHIPLOAD OF FIGHTING SAILORS

This exquisitely coloured balloon belongs not to just one animal but to a whole colony. The tentacles, sometimes thirty to forty feet long, have stinging organs with which the colony captures its food and defeats its enemies. You see Portuguese men-of-war at their loveliest when you are out in a boat. Those on shore are dead and have lost some of their iridescent colours; for a while, however, they may retain their ability to sting.

Atlantic coast. Nautical folk frequently refer to the members of this genus as "by-the-wind sailors", because they are always sailing before the wind.

JELLYFISHES

The Many-tentacled Jellyfish, *Zygodactyla groenlandica*, is one of the familiar jellyfishes seen along the Atlantic coast. It ranges from Greenland to the Carolinas. The circular mass of jelly-like material reaches a maximum diameter of about five inches. The mass is slightly depressed in the centre. About the edge and trailing downward are approximately one hundred tentacles ready to bring food into the animal's stomach. The stomach itself is a large tube, frilled around the edge, and extending downward from the centre of the medusa, or jelly cap. This mouth can be seen distinctly through the transparent jelly from above and serves as a quick means for identifying this species.

The genus comprises only one species. Northern specimens are transparent, but those in southern waters are tinted pink. Because of its numerous tentacles, some authors have named this animal the many-tentacled jellyfish.

The Flat Jellyfish, *Aequorea tenuis*, is a small species, scarcely two inches in diameter, with a flat umbrella. It also has many tentacles, eighty or more in number, but, since they are very fine, and the creature is small, they are hardly discernible. Although not common, this jellyfish may be seen in late summer along Long Island Sound.

Aequorea albida is found along the New England coast, also around Alaska and western Canada. Other species of the genus occur in the Mediterranean and Japanese seas, as well as in other waters of the world. When disturbed, many species of *Aequorea* show a luminescence from the base of their tentacles.

LARGE JELLYFISHES

Most abundant of the jellyfishes are those belonging to class Scyphozoa. This class, although rich in individuals, contains only about two hundred species. They are generally larger in size than those of the preceding class. Each one has four large reproductive organs, called gonads, arranged like a four-leaf clover in the centre of its umbrella. These are very conspicuous, and often brightly coloured.

The Common, or Moon, Jellyfish, *Aurelia aurita*, is undoubtedly the most abundant and widely distributed of the jellyfishes. That is why it is so popularly known as the common jellyfish. Its other name, moon jellyfish, it owes to its round, moonlike shape. From May to July, swarms of these jellyfishes float just below the surface in almost any backwater arm of the Atlantic and Pacific coasts. In early spring, they start life as tiny blobs of jelly. By midsummer, they have reached their maximum size of eight or ten inches. At this time, when mature, the gonads turn pink. Earlier, they are black, and are conspicuous as four circles sharply outlined in the white or blue-white of the jelly umbrella. These jellyfishes move laboriously by jerking pulsations as they alternately expand and contract this umbrella.

The Sea Blubber, *Cyanea capillata*, can be a large jellyfish. Although it is usually a foot or less in diameter, some are six or seven feet across. From its under-side eight groups of tentacles stream out. In the larger sea blubbers, these may reach a length of thirty or forty feet, and are capable of paralysing a swimmer. Widely distributed up and down the Atlantic and Pacific coasts of America, this jellyfish can be a serious menace to bathers. It is frequently washed ashore, or left stranded by the retreating tide, remaining on the sand as a mass of jelly. Its jelly is thicker and more resistant than that of most jellyfishes and, thus, persists longer. The colour of its umbrella varies from light yellow to brown. Individuals are sometimes bright pink or purplish. This bright colouring has caused the name sun jelly to be applied to the species.

Other Large Jellyfishes. *Stomolophus meleagris*, a small species about six or seven inches in diameter, is quite hemispherical in form. Brown in colour, it resembles a large, cone-shaped mushroom that has come to life and is swimming in the water. It lives in the warmer waters of the American Atlantic and Pacific coasts.

Rhopilema verrilli is also hemispherical and much larger in size. It frequently reaches a diameter of a foot or more. Although not common, it flaunts a yellow colour that makes it easily seen. It ranges from Long Island Sound southward into the warmer seas. *Rhopilema esculenta*, of eastern Asiatic waters, is the edible jellyfish highly prized by the Chinese and Japanese.

SEA ANEMONES AND STONY CORALS

Unlike other Coelenterata, the sea anemones and stony corals (class Anthozoa) have no medusa form. They exist only as polyps which make up the colony formation of the complete animal. The six thousand species all agree in being ocean-dwelling animals, but many of them differ so radically in shape that they would scarcely seem to be related. Most of them are fixed in place, and most have a skeleton composed either of lime or of a hornlike material called ceratine. Most of the species are found in the warmer waters of the world.

The Sea Fan, *Gorgonia flabellum*, is a colony secreting a skeleton of horny material, flat or fanlike in shape, with a single main stem. The blade, perforated with numerous openings, may be as much as two feet in height. Sea fans are common in the shallow waters of the West Indies and the warmer Atlantic Ocean regions. Yellow or reddish in colour, they were much sought after at one time as curiosities, or for decorative purposes. There are many other closely related species, all of them having their characteristic forms. One, *Gorgonia acerosa*, has tall, slender stems which are sometimes slightly branching.

The Red Coral, *Corallium nobile*, of the central and western Mediterranean Sea, is the commercial red coral used so extensively for jewellery a number of years ago, and now back in fashion. The colony, which reaches a height of about one foot, is profusely branching, and forms the very hard, slender twigs which, when broken, make the beads that are so familiar to everyone. Other species occur in the Atlantic Ocean and in Japanese waters. These, however, are not used as extensively for jewellery as the typical red coral.

The Yellowish Red Coral, *Alcyonium carneum*, is a curious relative of the red corals. Its greyish, limy skeleton is frequently cast up on the shores from New York to the Gulf of St. Lawrence, where it lives in waters ranging from low tide to several hundred feet in depth. It looks like a tiny, but heavy, treelike growth, three to four inches tall. When alive, these animals vary in colour from yellow to red.

The little yellow polyps that build up the skeleton are like tiny stars on the stubby branches of the colony. The skeleton is too coarse in grain and dull in colour, however, to have any commercial value.

Pennatula aculeata is the most common of the Sea Feathers, which get their names from their feather-like shape. They are seldom seen, for they inhabit the deeper waters, five hundred to three thousand feet, off the eastern coast of North America. Only about four inches high, they are a deep red in colour. Living in about the same depth of water off Nantucket and Newfoundland is *Pennatula grandis*. It reaches a height of fourteen inches, and its colour is a beautiful orange.

SEA ANEMONES

We now come to the sea anemones, which number about a thousand species. Looking like a beautiful underwater flower, the sea anemone has numerous outspread tentacles, usually brilliant in colour, which radiate from the top of a supporting stalk. When disturbed, the animal pulls in its tentacles and becomes a lumpy stump.

The Brown Anemone, *Metridium dianthus*, is the most common of the sea anemones and the largest among those found off the Atlantic coast between North Carolina and Labrador. It is also found in European waters. Four inches high, with a stalk nearly two and a half inches across, it spreads its yellowish tentacles like welcoming arms to any passing victim, in waters ranging from low tide to five hundred feet in depth. This species has won its common name, brown anemone, because of the brownish colour of the larger specimens.

Sagartia luciae is a tiny, but beautifully coloured, species. A slender creature, only half an inch high, it is light green, with about twelve vertical orange stripes on its body. From the top of its body radiate eighty-four tentacles arranged in four rows. This pretty creature is common in shallow water among rocks or in tidal pools from Florida to the Gulf of St. Lawrence, and also on the Pacific coast of the United States. Other species of *Sagartia*, equally beautiful, are found in all the waters of the world.

STONY CORALS

The stony corals are polyps which, sometimes singly, but usually in colonies, secrete a skeleton of calcareous material in the form of a cell into which the polyp can withdraw itself. The massing of these hard, stony skeletons forms the corals with which we are familiar. Those of the more temperate waters seldom result in the massive structures —whole islands of coral rising above the surface of the sea—which species in the tropical waters build up.

SEA ANEMONES—ANIMAL FLOWERS IN THE TIDAL POOLS

These little creatures are very lovely when they are waving their fringe of tentacles just below the surface of sunlit waters. Frighten them, and they huddle in unattractive stumps. A sea anemone usually has a broad, sucker-like foot for attaching itself to wharf posts, rocks, or even shells. But some live in sand, just below low water mark, and some can swim. Those along the Atlantic coast are in shades of brown, green, or yellow; those in tropical waters are more brightly coloured.

The Star Coral, *Astrangia danae*, develops a small, encrusting coral colony, of ten to thirty individuals, covering stones or other submerged objects. The little polyps, looking like tiny stars, are conspicuous as they lie embedded in the calcareous material. The coral patch may be four or five inches in diameter and about one-quarter of an inch thick, and is generally of a whitish colour. This creature is often washed ashore from the shallow waters, where it is common from Florida to New England. Another species is found on the Pacific coast. The encrusting corals are widely distributed and invade the colder waters of the world.

The genus *Porites* includes some of the more conspicuous branching corals. These are warm-water species, and are frequently reef-builders. Several species are common around Florida and in the West Indies.

Other corals are the fungus, or mushroom, corals, which get their name from their rounded or mushroom-like shape. Although the individuals are small, the resulting mass may be tremendous in size.

COMB JELLYFISHES

The Ctenophora are very soft jellyfishes, usually spherical or cylindrical in shape. They get their common name from their eight lengthwise rows of platelike cilia, or "combs". These are the organs of locomotion, which, through their waving, propel the organism through the surface waters of the seas. Although treated here as a class of the Coelenterata, the Ctenophora are considered a separate phylum by many zoologists.

The Common Comb Jellyfish, *Mnemiopsis leidyi*, is a colourless, nearly transparent jellyfish, three inches long and one inch in diameter. It is abundant from the New England coast southward to the Carolinas. Late in the summer, these jellyfishes sometimes become so numerous in the back bays and inlets along the coast that the water feels thick and gelatinous to swimmers who venture in at this time. At night they glow beautifully with a phosphorescent blue light as they swim slowly and sedately along. This is especially true when the water is agitated by a passing boat or even by a hand swept through the water. A smaller species, *Mnemiopsis gardeni*, one and a half inches long, and a translucent blue in colour, is found from Chesapeake Bay to Florida.

The Sea Walnut, *Pleurobrachia pileus*, is a small sphere of transparent jelly less than one inch in diameter. Its notable features are two six-inch tentacles, white or bright rose in colour, which stream out into the water. These tentacles are extremely beautiful when observed closely, for each is feathered along one side with very fine, long threads. The sea walnut is common, during August and September, from Long Island to Greenland, as well as in European waters, and along the American Pacific coast. Other species occur elsewhere.

Beroë ovata, about four inches in length, is a common and nearly cosmopolitan species. Along the Atlantic coast, it ranges from Chesapeake Bay southward. The more northern forms are pink, while those in the south are milky white. *Beroë cucumis* is found in great abundance from Long Island Sound north to Labrador, and also on the Pacific coast. It is about the same size as *ovata*, but has a slight neck behind its mouth. Its colour is a beautiful rose. This species is frequently called the northern comb jelly; but the more appropriate name of sea mitre or mitre jellyfish is often used because of its resemblance to a mitre. *Beroë forskali* is twice as long, or nearly eight inches. More conical in shape, it tapers from its mouth to a blunt point. This species is found along the Pacific coast and in the Mediterranean Sea.

Moss Animals and Lamp Shells

MOSS ANIMALS OR BRYOZOANS

LIKE THE sponges and the corals, the moss animals (phylum Bryozoa) usually live in colonies.

The individual animal is small and roundish, or cylindrical, with a bunch of waving tentacles protruding from its limey covering. After the death of the animal or colony, the covering remains, like coral or the shell of a mollusc.

The colonies of some species form mosslike patches on stones, on logs, and even on other sea animals, such as corals and sponges. Some of the larger colony-making species, consisting of thousands of individuals, branch and re-branch until they take on the appearance of miniature, leafless trees. So plantlike in appearance are the bryozoans that early naturalists regarded them as seaweeds.

All bryozoans are water animals. Of the known species, over three thousand make their homes in the ocean, while less than fifty live in fresh water. While all of them are interesting to study, many of them are especially so, for they are coloured, or iridescent, with yellow, orange, pink, or red. Examine carefully any submerged object, such as seaweeds, stones, logs, piles, and floating wharves, and you will surely find one or more bryozoan colonies.

The Seaweed Crust, genus *Flustrella*, is commonly seen on many of the seaweeds. It forms a small patch, gauzy or lacy in appearance. The Hyaline Encrusting Bryozoan, *Schizoporella hyalina*, is a glossy-appearing species. It builds successive layers of translucent material, usually on submerged stones or logs.

Another, the Silvery Encrusting Bryozoan, genus *Membranipora*, is easily recognized by its somewhat circular patches of gleaming silver on small submerged stones.

The *Lichenopora* form small, lichen-like spots, one-half inch or less in diameter, on stones or shells. The spots are usually grey or yellow in colour.

The genus *Crisia* contains a number of small species commonly found on stones, shells, or other submerged objects. Only ten inches or so tall, they look like tiny, branching plants, with miniature leaves covering the stems. Yellow or yellow-brown is their usual colour. The Bushy Grey Bryozoan, *Crisia eburnea*, is a common species along the Atlantic coast.

We find the giants of the group in the genus *Bugula*, for some of its species actually reach a height of one foot or more. They occur throughout the waters of the world, and may be found on submerged objects, from low-tide mark to one hundred or more feet below the surface. Each is a colony of thousands of individual animals, all of which wave their tentacles and feed independently.

The Fern Bryozoan, *Bugula turrita*, is the species commonly found along the Atlantic coast, from Maine to the Carolinas. So called because of its delicate, fernlike growth, it has a lower stem of orange, and upper parts of yellow. A number of years ago there was considerable commercial activity in dredging up these growths, drying them, then spraying them a bright green, and selling them as Christmas decorations. In this form they acquired the name of "air fern".

LAMP SHELLS

While wandering along the coastal beaches of America, one frequently sees, washed up on the sand, what appear to be tiny clam shells, about one-half inch long. A delicate yellow in colour, they are thin and translucent, so thin and fragile that it is difficult to find a perfect example. Because of their shell-like appearance (and they have fooled many experts), they have been given the name "lamp shell". Most of them belong to the genus *Terebratulina*. Closely related to the Bryozoa, the lamp shells are put in a separate phylum called Brachiopoda ("having arms and feet").

Starfishes, Sea Urchins, and Their Kin

ANYONE who can walk along a sea beach, or at least any sea beach not too close to the filth of our cities, has a fine opportunity to observe some members of the phylum Echinodermata, the "spiny-skinned" animals. Starfishes and sea urchins glide imperceptibly over the sands at low tide. Occasionally, you can see a brittle star walking stiltlike on the tips of its points. Storms, especially along the warmer coasts, are sure to toss up on the beach for your amazement feather stars, sea lilies, and sea cucumbers, from their deep-water homes.

If you live inland, you can see collections of these animals in most museums, for the calcareous shells or skeletons are easily preserved, and a large collection is highly interesting from many points of view.

Indeed, to get any overall picture of the Echinodermata phylum, you will need to see a large collection of its members. If you do, you will notice an important feature that the casual beach-walker would miss, namely, that the five-sidedness, which is so obvious in the starfish, is also present in a camouflaged, or imperfect, manner throughout the whole phylum.

Labels and charts in the museum will inform you of the great geological age of the Echinodermata, and of the great number of extinct species that have been found. This is a group that at an early period diverged markedly from the other groups, and then evolved along a line all its own. In having few connecting links with other animal life, the Echinodermata are like the sponges.

The phylum readily divides into five main divisions or classes: Asteroidea, comprising the starfishes; Echinoidea, the sea urchins; Ophiuroidea, the brittle stars; Crinoidea, the feather stars and sea lilies; and Holothurioidea, the sea cucumbers.

Over five thousand species are known. They inhabit all of our seas and oceans, except the very coldest, with most of the species preferring the warmer waters.

STARFISHES—NOT FISHES AT ALL

Some persons have laboured to establish the term "sea stars" for these creatures, and there is no doubt that it is an apter name. But, although they are not fishes in any sense of the word, the term "starfishes" has been used so long that it is impossible to change it now.

Most of the many species of this group (class Asteroidea) are plentiful along the coast of the United States and Europe. During high tide, they travel up the beach and then are left stranded, to die in the sun as the tide retreats. Rocky tidal pools are good places to observe them, for, frequently, dozens, representing a number of species, will be left in one of these miniature seas. If they are fortunate and the pool does not dry up, the returning tide will allow them to travel on and perhaps get back into deeper water.

The five-pointed body is characteristic of most of the starfishes. A few have six points, however, and others have as many as ten, or more, points. In some, the space between the points is filled in, making a nearly perfect pentagon. The upper surface of a starfish is covered with blunt spines. Near the junction of two of the points, or arms, as they are called, is a porous plate called the sieve plate. Through this plate, water enters the ring canal, then flows into the five, or more, radial canals that extend out into the arms. The under-side of each arm is fitted with sucker-like processes, called ampullae, or tube-feet, which are moved by the hydraulic action of the circulating water.

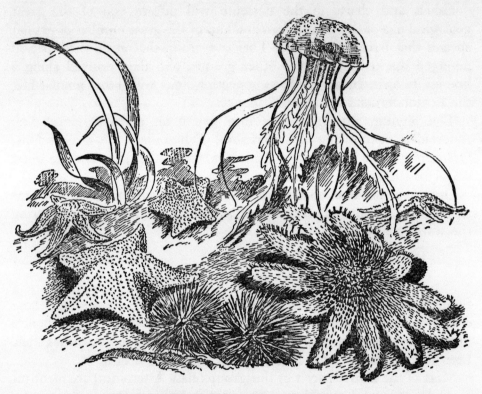

SEA STARS, SEA URCHINS, AND A JELLYFISH

Most sea stars, or starfishes, are five-pointed, but a few, like the sunburst sea star pictured at the lower right, have from eight to fourteen points (the huge Alaskan sea star, not shown here, may have as many as twenty-four points). The burrlike creatures are sea urchins, or sea porcupines. One of the Florida jellyfishes is shown at the upper right.

HOW STARFISHES MOVE

Starfishes walk in any direction, with the arm on the direction side taking the lead, a process which makes them amusing to watch. The tip of one arm curls up, then pushes out. Slowly, the animal slides forward as this lead arm contracts. If turned on its back, the starfish will lie quietly, as if it had no idea what to do. Then, with scarcely any perceptible movement, one arm, sometimes more, will curve backward until the tip touches the ground. Curving more and more, it presses flatter and flatter to the ground. Another arm follows in a similar manner. Meanwhile, the arms on the other side are curving higher and higher. The creature is now almost on edge. A little more now, the balance swings to the other side, and the starfish flops **over**, right side up.

This ability to turn over is not the only accomplishment of the starfish, for it is a remarkably versatile creature. It is able to squeeze through a crevice no wider than one of its arms. With one arm leading the way, the creature will elongate the remainder of its body and drag itself through the narrow opening. The starfish also has the peculiar habit of raising its body from the ground and standing on the tips of its arms, as if preparing to trip off to a dance.

IMPATIENT EATERS

The mouth of the starfish is on its ventral, or bottom, side, in the centre, at the spot where the arms meet. A starfish feeds largely on shellfish, and it shows a special preference for clams and oysters. Although the starfish moves slowly, the clam is much slower in ploughing through the mud, and the starfish soon overtakes it.

The starfish is an impatient eater and swallows small shellfish and molluscs whole. Absorbing the edible parts, it evacuates the hard, indigestible remains through its mouth. It uses its arms to deal with larger clams, encircling them and attaching its sucker-like ampullae firmly to the smooth surface of the clamshell. Then, with steadily increasing force, the starfish begins to pull the two shells apart. Eventually, even the biggest mussels, which can resist larger and stronger creatures, give way before this continuous pressure and slowly open. The starfish then literally turns its stomach inside out and extends it into the shell, surrounding and devouring the body of the clam.

When starfishes invade oyster beds, they cause a tremendous amount of destruction. The oyster fishermen of a few generations back thought they were wreaking vengeance on their enemy when they tore a captured starfish in two and tossed the parts back into the ocean. It remained for the research scientist to discover that, instead of destroying this pest, the fishermen were helping to increase its numbers, for a starfish can regenerate all its missing parts, and may even regenerate an entire animal from a single arm.

The Common Starfish, *Asterias vulgaris*, is also called the purple starfish because of its deep violet colour. The sieve plate, or madreporite, is yellow or grey. This species is common along the New England coast. Some grow to the diameter of a foot or more.

Forbes's Starfish, *Asterias forbesi*, replaces *vulgaris* farther south along the Atlantic seaboard. It is greenish, with a bright-orange sieve plate. At the tip of each arm is a red eyespot. Its arms and body are more convex, or arched, than those of *vulgaris*, which tends to be flattish. A full-grown adult is seldom over six inches across.

The Scarlet Starfish, *Hippasteria pharygiana*, is bright scarlet in colour when alive. Although not much over eight inches in diameter, it is a very convex and heavy species, for it has short, stocky arms and a large central region. This species lives in rather deep water, and is seldom seen along the beach, except after a violent storm which has stirred the ocean to its depths.

The Common Sun Star, *Crossaster papposus*, is quickly identified by its many short, thick arms. These arms may vary in number from eight to fourteen. Nearly six inches in diameter, it is of a rich, purple colour that becomes lighter toward the centre. It lives in shallow water, as well as in the deeper parts of the sea. The Pacific coast is the home of a number of similar species, such as the sunflower star and Dawson's sun star.

Other Starfish. From the thick-armed species we go to the slender-armed. The Common Slender Starfish, *Leptasterias tenera*, is one of these. Only about three inches across, it varies in colour from grey to violet. The Red Slender Starfish, *Henricia sanguinolenta*, is also a common species in shallow waters and varies from yellow to a reddish colour. It has a smoother surface than that of *Leptasterias tenera*. A very similar species, *Henricia laeviuscula*, is common on the Pacific coast. This slenderness of the arms reaches its maximum in the Ophiuroidea, or brittle stars, which we will meet later.

The coralline Bryozoa take their name from their external resemblance to coral structures. Most Bryozoan colonies are quite small and have definite limy skeletons which remain behind when the individual or colony dies. Some 2,500 extinct species are recognized in different geologic strata dating back to earliest times. Many of these ancient species lived over short periods of time, geologically speaking, but had wide geographic distribution, so their fossil remains are useful in correlating geologic strata and achieve some economic importance in the study of cores brought up from test drilling for oil wells. *See page 1673*

[13-15]

[13-15A]

The Brachiopods, commonly known as lampshells, are placed in a phylum by themselves. While they have paired shells similar to the clams and mussels, these little animals are oriented "top and bottom" rather than laterally as are the molluscs. The bottom shell is generally larger and has an extension through which protrudes the "foot" by which the animal anchors itself permanently to the sea bottom. It is from this ventral shell which resembles ancient Roman household lamps that their common name derives. The 225 living species are only a small remnant of the once numerous animals whose fossil records go back some 400 million years. Various species venture to depths of 18,000 feet with the Bryozoa. *See page 1674*

[13-16]

The common starfish—which is not a fish at all—is most abundant along the New England coast and is one of the larger varieties, growing to a diameter of a foot or more. Starfishes usually swallow small shellfish and molluscs whole, absorbing the edible parts and evacuating the indigestible remains through the mouth. They open larger clams and mussels by encircling them with their arms, attaching the sucker-like ampullae to the smooth shell and drawing the two halves apart. Several species range the East and West Coasts of North America and do considerable damage when they invade the oyster and clam beds. *See page 1678*

[13-16A]

Dawson's sun star is a Pacific Coast variety. Many species have more than five arms, and in some the space between the points is filled in. The upper surface is generally covered with rough spines. The mouth is in the centre on the underside and the ventral surface of each arm is fitted with the "suction cup" tube-feet. There is no head, but the tip of each arm is equipped with a light-sensitive eye spot and a small, soft tactile tentacle. Starfishes move in any direction, the arm on the direction side taking the lead. Although they are fairly complex organisms, an entire animal may be regenerated from a single arm. *See page 1674*

More Trees and How to Know Them

THE HORSE-CHESTNUT

THIS tree must be familiar to many people in Britain, who would be surprised to know that it is a European plant introduced here only a few hundred years ago. Although it has shiny brown seeds enclosed in a spiny cover like the true Chestnut, the two trees are not closely related. The leaves of the Horse-Chestnut appear very early in the spring and are followed by the beautiful heads of flowers. The flowers have large white petals, blotched with yellow and pink, and outspread stamens. The tree becomes covered with them; they stand up like giant candles.

It is claimed that the seeds of the horse-chestnut were used long ago as medicine for horses—hence the tree's name. When the green prickly balls encasing the fruit open in the autumn, the highly polished reddish-brown nuts become the prized treasures of children.

In June and July you find the horse-chestnut tree at its loveliest; showy white flower clusters from six to twelve inches high appear then and the leaves are fully developed. Its leaves suggest tropical foliage in their size and luxuriance, for leaflets from five to seven inches long are grouped together like a palm with six or seven fingers. Its bark is dark brown, with deep furrows and scaly ridges.

The winter twigs of horse-chestnut are easy to recognize. Very bumpy in outline, they have distinct horseshoe-shaped scars below the buds; the buds themselves are shining brown and very sticky. If the twigs are stood in water in early spring the unfolding of the young hairy leaves can be observed over the ensuing weeks.

THE LUXURIANT FOLIAGE OF THE HORSE-CHESTNUT

This favourite shade tree carries a suggestion of tropical growth in the size and profusion of its leaves and its showy flower clusters. Now a well-known British tree, it was originally found in Balkan countries and introduced into England four hundred years ago. Though inedible and despised even by squirrels, this tree's shiny nuts are prized by children.

The Cone-Bearing Trees

FIRS FOR CHRISTMAS

The firs are so closely associated with the delights of Christmas that children are likely to be particularly interested in these trees. We cannot help admiring the symmetrical form and rich dark green colour. Unfortunately the narrow needle-like leaves which in nature stay so long on the tree soon fall in the hot, dry atmosphere of the living room. In America, people avoid this by using at Christmas another tree, the Balsam Fir, which retains its leaves.

Our Christmas tree is the Norway Spruce, introduced from Europe. The narrow, hard leaves are a characteristic it shares with most of the members of a large group of plants. This group are called Conifers because, instead of having flowers, their seeds are produced on a series of hard scales which form a cone. The needle-like leaves do not fall at the end of the growing season as do those of the broad-leaved trees; for this reason they are spoken of as "evergreen" and even called "the Evergreens" in North America.

We have only three conifers native in this country, but many others are cultivated for ornament and profit. Their timber, too, is characteristic, and forms the so-called softwood of the building trade. The conifers are also collectively called fir trees, but it would be more precise to keep "Fir" as the name of only one of the kinds, using, for example, Spruce for those most like the Christmas Tree, and Pine for those like our Scots Pine.

Canada Balsam. The Balsam Fir yields a useful product: Canada balsam, used in making turpentine. The balsam comes from resin blisters under the thick rich brown bark which are a great fire hazard for the trees. In case of fire, the resin quickly turns the whole tree into a torch.

SPRUCES—ONCE USED FOR CHEWING GUM

Several kinds of spruce have a wide range in North America—from coast to coast, as far south as West Virginia and as far north as Labrador and Alaska. Young spruces are often used as Christmas trees, despite the fact that they shed their needles early in a warm house; but you do not often see them adorning landscapes. As cultivated trees they are relatively short-lived and their dead branches give them an uneven appearance.

Children are usually intrigued to know that spruce resin was once an important source of chewing gum—now replaced by *chicle* from the tropics. The North American Indians used spruce gum to waterproof their canoes.

(*Left*) THE BALSAM FIR MEANS CHRISTMAS IN NORTH AMERICA

To American children the fragrant balsam tree means Christmas. Outdoors, the fir, with its straight trunk and graceful, symmetrical branches, adorns many a landscape of Canada and the northern United States. The balsam fir is particularly attractive in wintry surroundings, when it is effectively outlined against a snowy background. It is not a long-lived tree; it seldom survives ninety years.

(*Right*) THE SPRUCE AND ITS VARIED FORMS

There are many kinds of spruce trees. The American black spruce, above, varies its shape according to the natural forces with which it has to contend. On lowlands the spruce grows narrow and tall; on mountains it becomes dwarfed—no more than five feet tall. The cones of this spruce may remain on the tree for decades.

Apart from the Norway Spruce, there are others grown in Great Britain, two of which you may find in parks and gardens, or growing in quantity in plantations. One is the Sitka Spruce, which comes from the Pacific coast of North America; it is cultivated into dense plantations of beautifully straight trees with few branches. Serbian Spruce has rather short, drooping branches so that its fir-tree shape becomes narrow and spire-like.

OUR NATIVE CONIFERS

Of the three conifers which grow wild in Great Britain, only two are trees. (The third is the Juniper.) Our two trees are members of quite different groups of conifers: the Scots Pine is one of a genus which has orthodox cones and needle-like leaves, whereas the Yew has its seeds on an organ hardly recognizable as a cone at all, and its leaves are strap-shaped.

THE SCOTS PINE

Scots Pine is a native of the Scottish Highlands, but is well established as a naturalized tree on heathy ground in many parts of Britain. The trees are well-branched when young, but in age the lower branches are lost, and the result is a tall tree with a spreading crown on an almost naked trunk. The leaves are developed on very short side-shoots, each of which bears a pair of leaves, two or three inches long, encircled at the base by a papery sheath. Among the tuft of leaves at the ends of the twigs you can find the yellow clusters of male organs. The female organ, which will become the cone, is very insignificant at first near the apex of the year-old shoot. After fertilization, the conelet develops over the next two years into the hard, woody cone, an inch or more long. The winged seeds are borne in pairs on the upper side of the cone-scales. Our Scots Pine is only one of a large number of Pine species.

THE SOMBRE YEW

The Yew, though only moderately tall, spreads widely, forming a low, thick, dark crown. The trunk is fluted, dividing soon into numerous boughs. The Yew's leaves are scarcely an inch long, and their short stalks are twisted so that the twigs bear a flat fan on either side. The trees are either male or female. The male trees produce series of tufts of yellow male catkins among the leaves. The female cone is quite small at first, consisting of an ovule enveloped in a number of green scales.

After fertilization, the circlet of scales gives rise to a swollen, red, fleshy organ called an aril, which surrounds the seed.

The yew, unlike the Scots Pine, is commoner in the south of Britain; it occurs scattered all over Europe, and even reaches North Africa and the Himalayas. You will often find it planted: it forms good hedges when clipped, and seems to have been a favourite for planting in churchyards. Yew wood is ideal for making archers' bows; there was a time, therefore, when yew trees were a military necessity.

The yew is a sombre-looking tree and many superstitions are held about it. But its poison is no superstition; many people and even more animals have died from it. The leaves, the seeds, the bark, almost the whole tree, contains a deadly poison.

PINES OF THE REST OF THE WORLD

Some pine trees reach a height of two hundred feet—and even more. An age of two hundred years is not unusual, and the sturdiness of pine wood makes it particularly suitable for the masts of ships. And pines are handsome too. Branches of the white pine make especially graceful decorations.

The branches of pines are all attractive: this graceful quality derives from their length and also from the way that the needles are attached to the branches in bundles.

Needles—The Key to Identification. The pines can generally be distinguished from other conifers by their longer needles. The grouping of the needles provides a key to the various species because the number varies from one type of pine to another. For example, those called white pines have five needles to a bundle; the pitch, red, and ponderosa pines generally have three; and others, like our Scots Pine, have needles grouped in pairs. Some pine needles are long, soft and pliable; those of the pitch pine and some others are stiff and coarse.

The shape of pine needles is such that the wind blowing through them makes the soft sighing sound that we like to fancy as the trees whispering.

The "whispering pines" and other cone-bearing evergreens were growing on earth long before the more modern type of tree—the deciduous or "leaf-dropping" kind, which sheds its foliage each year—

(Left) THE SCOTS PINE

Our native pine is thought to have been naturally widespread all over Britain long ago, but now occurs truly wild only in Scotland. It survives naturally all over Europe, however, from Lapland to the Mediterranean. The needles are in pairs—flat above, rounded below; the cones are less than two inches long, and stand erect from the stem.

(Right) THE MAJESTIC WHITE PINE

The magnificent American Pine reaches a height of two hundred feet and may live two hundred years or more. It is very easy to identify by its needles, which are bluish green, from three to five inches long, and grow in groups of five. The cones are from four to eight inches long and droop gracefully.

and they have clung to their ancient custom of retaining their needle-like leaves all year round.

Pine Cones. Boys and girls enjoy gathering the cones of evergreens. Some of these cones are splendid collector's pieces. Small ones may be painted or used in natural colour for Christmas trimmings; larger cones, such as those of the American sugar pine, which weigh a pound or more, are spectacular items for nature collections.

Pine cones, which develop from small pistillate flowers, require two years to mature. In May and June you can see the bright pink flowers of white pine growing near the tips of new twigs. On the new shoots of lower branches, yellow staminate conelike blossoms appear and produce quantities of pollen. Soon after this pollen has been carried off by the wind, these blossoms wither and fall; but meanwhile the pistillate flowers, which have been pollinated, are beginning to turn into cones.

By the end of a season's growth the cones are about an inch long, green and upright. By the second season they are longer and turn downward. By August they have turned brown and are from five to eleven inches in length. If you look at them carefully at this time, you will find two little winged seeds beneath each scale. In September the cone scales open out and the wind carries the seeds away—perhaps as far as a quarter of a mile.

MASSIVE SEQUOIAS—THOUSANDS OF YEARS OLD

The natural place to find these huge trees is in the national parks of California, though giant sequoias have been successfully planted in other parts of California and occasionally in parts of the eastern United States and Europe.

The sequoia is the most massive, as well as the oldest, of all living things. Some of the very trees that stand majestically today on the high slopes of the Sierras were growing in the time of Christ—roughly two thousand years ago. Some sequoias are more than three hundred feet high! These magnificent trees were named in honour of Sequoyah, a gifted Indian chief who invented an alphabet over a hundred years ago for his people of the Cherokee tribe.

The Sequoia's Foliage and Bark. The rich evergreen foliage is in the form of scalelike sharp-pointed needles that overlap closely on the branches. The tiny flowers are produced in February or March. From the seed-producing conelets there develop yellowish-brown, egg-shaped cones between two and three inches long. These mature in two years and the seeds are blown away, but the empty cones often remain on the tree. Sequoias are better able to resist fire than other trees because their spongy red-brown bark is at least twelve inches thick—sometimes as much as twenty-four—on mature trees.

The Towering Redwood. The giant sequoia has a cousin, the towering redwood, which grows to an even greater height—though its girth is less than that of the sequoia. The redwood gets its name from the straight-grained red wood which varies in tone from light cherry to dark mahogany. It is a popular wood for building. As in the case of the sequoia, the thick fibrous bark is exceptionally fire-resistant. It is reddish grey with fissures running up and down the trunk, giving it a fluted appearance.

An American conifer which can often be seen planted in Britain is the Swamp Cypress. Curiously for a conifer, its light feathery leaves turn brown in the autumn and fall. Although called a cypress, it is not of the same genus as our true garden cypresses.

The Swamp Cypress grows into a tall pyramidal tree with beautiful pale green foliage. It presents a striking effect in winter because one is not used to the coniferous growth form lacking leaves. It comes from the southern United States and prefers damp situations; in this country it is often planted beside water. When you find one, look out for the peculiar knee-shaped organs rising from the roots and breaking ground around the bole.

How to Mount Evergreen Specimens

Youngsters can make attractive exhibits of evergreens with little or no aid. You start by finding a shallow cardboard box and cutting a square out of the lid, leaving a half-inch margin around the edge. Fill the box with cottonwool, right up to the top. Place the evergreen spray on this, removing just enough of the cotton under the stem so that the spray will lie flat.

Now place a piece of glass over the square opening in the lid and fasten it neatly with a tape binding. Put the lid on the box and fasten it by inserting pins on all four sides. You can of course decorate or paint the box in advance, and the tape may be coloured to provide an even more handsome setting.

Flowers on Trees and Shrubs

When we look forward to flowers that bloom in the spring, we usually have in mind the small, shy blossoms of woodlands and meadows. However, certain trees make a gorgeous if brief display with their flowers. If a botanical garden or well-stocked park is within reasonable travelling distance of your home, you will be well rewarded if you keep track of the best time to see them. There is a great delight in viewing the massed array of their colours.

Most of the trees that have been discussed have insignificant flowers, but there are many that are cultivated for their colourful display— Cherries, for instance, which produce a mass of blossom. Do look for them, as well as for the many cultivated flowering bushes. Many people think the Magnolia the most beautiful, with its strikingly large pink and white flowers, large leaves and smooth bark.

In the wild we have a number of shrubs which give a good display, though mostly of white flowers only. Elder, for example, with its large clusters of tiny blossoms; it has leaves divided into five or seven leaflets, and the fruits are small and black. Another is Dogwood, more common in southern England, which has rather loose clusters of unpleasantly scented flowers. Its leaves are somewhat oblong, and when torn show strands of gum between the broken veins. A native tree with attractive flowers is the Rowan. This has leaves with more than ten leaflets, and its flower-cluster is creamy white; later in the year you may easily spot its shining, bright-red fruits.

APPLE BLOSSOMS

The blossoms of apple and other fruit trees make a lovely floral display. Children can appreciate the individual beauty of an apple tree in bloom, if they examine the cluster of blossoms that grows at the tip of each twig. With soft green leaves surrounding each cluster, the effect is that of a conventional bouquet. By contrast, peach and cherry blossoms grow along the sides of the branches.

Though we find five, six, or even more blossoms in a cluster of apple blossoms, only one or two of each tend to develop into fruit. It is interesting to examine an apple and a blossom together, observing the parts of the flower that may still be seen in the fruit. The five scales at the apple's smaller end are the remains of the calyx lobes that originally enclosed the blossom; and within them are the dried and shrunken stamens and styles.

You will find many buds on an apple tree branch that produce only leaves; whereas at the side and below the spur (where the apple develops), there is a bud that will continue the growth of the branch. The following year the blossom buds will break out along this new growth.

Shrubs and Bushes

HOW TO TELL A SHRUB FROM A TREE

It is not easy to be exact enough to satisfy a boy or girl who wants to know the difference between a shrub and a tree. Both shrubs and trees are woody, perennial plants. Trees are generally much larger— but you may find some shrubs, such as the blackthorn, almost rivalling a small plum tree in size. There is a definite line of cleavage, however, in that trees have a single trunk, whereas shrubs are divided into many primary stems at the ground, or near it.

THE HAWTHORN—FLOWERS IN MAY

This very common and attractive plant is not a very characteristic shrub, for it can form a respectable tree; but you will most often find it as a shrub. It is very common; the hedgerows of Britain must contain thousands. Early in spring its spiny branches are covered with tight, many-flowered bunches of white, strongly-scented flowers. The leaves are small and dark green, with a few irregular lobes; the tree is characteristically thorny, the thorns being really very short branches. The fruits are bright red, and contain a single hard stone.

Two kinds of hawthorn can be found; the one described above is the commoner one. The best way to recognize it is to find the single style which rises from the cup-like centre of the flower; it also has a larger bunch of flowers, with perhaps as many as twenty. The less common hawthorn, found mostly in the midland and southern counties of England, has more than one style and fewer flowers in the bunch, often no more than ten. When the fruits are present, you can find two stones inside instead of the Common Hawthorn's one.

WILD COUSINS OF OUR GARDEN PLANTS

There are shrubs which are the wild relations of some of our garden fruit and flower bushes. You will immediately recognize wild roses by their similarity to the cultivated kinds. The commonest is the Dog Rose with small pink or red flowers. Its scent is slight, far exceeded by that of the Sweet Briar, which has brighter flowers. You may also find the Field Rose, which has almost snow-white petals and, if you are not too far from the coast, the Burnet Rose, which is easy to recognize by its very prickly and even spiny stems, and almost black fruit.

Raspberries, blackberries and gooseberries, and even black currants can be found in wild places, but no one is very sure if all the kinds found are really native plants in Britain. Never mind, their fruits are good, and worth finding. You may have gathered wild blackberries and know their fine flavour; the wild raspberry also has a very pleasant taste. You will be able to recognize them if you know the garden shrubs. When you examine them, compare their growth; notice how the raspberry throws up long "canes" and how the blackberry flowers on the growth of the previous year, and so on.

Woody plants—that is, shrubs and trees—have different characteristic ways of growing.

SHRUBS OF THE PEA FAMILY

Do you know the flowers of the Pea, or perhaps of the Sweet Pea? There are many plants with this kind of flower; it has a boat-shaped centre, a pair of wings on either side, and a large petal standing up at the back. Two common wild shrubs are of this family of plants: Gorse and Broom.

Gorse forms a straggly bush some six feet or more tall, covered with rigid, branched spines. Bright golden-yellow scented flowers adorn the ends of the branches. You'll find it on heaths and commons all over Britain, and if you sit very quietly among the bushes late in the season you may actually hear the brown, hairy pods bursting to scatter the seeds. The stems are straight and angular, with rather scattered, small, elliptic leaves. Broom is widespread in Britain, but not as common as gorse, because it is confined to neutral or acid soils. It too has explosive pods, longer than those of gorse, and black when ripe.

THE JUNIPER AND ITS FALSE BERRY

Our native coniferous shrub, the Juniper, is more common in the south of England but can be found throughout Britain. It forms a dense bush with half-inch long flat, needle-like striped leaves. It may be quite tall, up to fifteen feet or more, but also occurs in a low, almost creeping form. The plants are either male or female. The female produces minute cone-like clusters of scale leaves, the central ones of which develop into the blue-black organ, the so-called juniper berry. If you examine these closely you can find the tiny tips of the swollen scales; the "berry" is really a very fleshy cone with a few hard seeds buried within.

Making Leaf Collections

Children, as we know, are avid collectors; and collecting leaves often provides a completely satisfying outlet for this instinct. They can obtain foliage of many kinds of trees in late summer and early autumn by simply picking the leaves off the ground. To preserve them, place each leaf between sheets of newspaper, with several sheets above and more below, and with a heavy weight on top of the pile. In a few days the leaf will be dried out and flattened so that it can be fastened in a scrapbook with glue and narrow strips of paper.

HOW TO MAKE SPATTER PRINTS

Older boys and girls may enjoy the more elaborate process of making leaf prints. There are several methods.

Possibly the simplest method is the spatter print, which requires the use of ink, a toothbrush, a small piece of wire screening (or a thin stick), sheets of paper, and fresh—not dried—leaves.

First place the leaf on a sheet of paper and pin it down absolutely flat. Then dip the toothbrush into the ink, remove it and allow the surplus to drain back into the bottle. Now, working from side to side and from top to bottom of the paper, hold the brush a few inches above it and rub the bristles against the wire screening (or stick) to spatter the ink. Scrape the bristles *toward* you, as this throws the ink in the opposite direction. (It may be a good idea to let the youngster practise this stroke several times before trying it with ink.)

When the whole surface of the paper is covered, you can finally remove the leaf—and what remains is a perfect outline of the leaf, surrounded by hundreds of little spatters of ink.

HOW TO MAKE PRINTS WITH PRINTER'S INK

Leaf prints made with printer's ink have the advantage over spatter prints that they show not only the outline of the leaf but also many of its veins. The materials you need for this third process are: a tube of printer's ink (any colour), a sheet of window glass slightly larger than the leaves, a rubber roller, and paper.

Roll out a thick film of ink on the surface of the glass. Next place the leaf, with its under-side down, on this inked surface. Put a piece of paper over the leaf and work the roller over it several times. Now you can discard the paper and lift the leaf from the ink.

To make your print, place the leaf, with the inked side down, on a sheet of clean paper. Place another sheet of paper over it and work the roller back and forth directly over the paper-covered leaf. Now remove the top paper and leaf and allow the finished print to dry.

When the youngster has made a series of leaf prints or mounted the actual leaves, his collection will mean a great deal more to him if he labels each leaf with the name and a few short notes about the characteristics of the tree on which it grew, the time of year, perhaps, and where the tree was growing.

Growing Trees At Home

Apart from the pleasure of observing trees in their natural environment and in decorative landscapes, it is also fun to watch them start growing from seed. It is far more difficult to get tree seeds to grow

INK SPATTERING   BLUEPRINT   PRINTER'S INK PRINT

than flower seeds; even under natural conditions only one out of thousands may develop into a tree. But if you keep certain facts in mind, you should have a rewarding measure of success.

Among the better seeds to try your green thumb with are acorns, horse-chestnuts, sycamore, and beech seeds. They germinate quickly and, if successful, they put forth their first leaves the spring after they are planted. You can prepare ground in flowerpots or flat, lightweight wooden boxes such as the ones used for packing certain kinds of cheese. If you use the box, make several drainage holes in the bottom and cover them with broken bits of pottery, rounded sides up, so that the holes will not become clogged.

Now put a layer of pebbles over the bottom of the box or pot, followed by garden soil and sand, mixed half and half, until the box is filled to within half an inch from the top—and press down firmly. Plant the seeds, place a light covering of soil over them, and press the soil down again. (Such seeds as acorns and chestnuts should be soaked in water for two days before planting.)

Keep your "tree garden" very close to a window which admits plenty of sunshine. The soil, which should be kept moist but never wet, is best watered with a bulb spray or sprinkler. Until the seeds sprout, it is helpful to cover the top with a pane of glass, thus preventing the surface from drying out.

You can keep small trees in pots for years. They remain dwarfed and do not flower, but otherwise they are as interesting as forest trees. If you have land with space for more trees, it is naturally a thrilling experience for a child to transplant one of the seedlings in its second year to the out-of-doors, where it may soon outdistance him in growth!